1000

of the World's Greatest

BRAINBUSTERS

First published in Great Britain in 2002 by
Dean, an imprint of Egmont Books Limited,
239 Kensington High Street,
London W8 6SA

Copyright © 2002 Egmont Books Limited

ISBN 0 603 56068 7

1 3 5 7 9 10 8 6 4 2

Printed and bound in the U.A.E.

1000

of the World's Greatest

BRAINBUSTERS

Written and Compiled by: Guy Campbell & Mark Devins
Illustrated by: Paul Moran & Simon Ecob

WORDOODLES

Say what you see

Each of these Wordoodles is a word, phrase or saying, cunningly disguised! For example:

"minI'LL BE THEREute"

would mean: "I'll be there in a minute!"

See how you get on with these...

1. Pot O O O O O O O O

2. bad bad

3. knee
   light light

4. chawho'srge

5. ONCE
   4:56pm

6. injury + insult

7. welieight

8. garplayden

9. XQQME

10. Must get here
    Must get here
    Must get here

SOLUTIONS

SHORT & SWEET
Figures of Speech

Here is a bunch of well known phrases involving numbers. Each has been shortened to just numbers and initials. For example: "26 = L of the A" would be 26 Letters of the Alphabet. We'll supply a few clues; see how you get on with these...

1. 12 = S of the Z
    Clue: Leo

2. 11 = P in a F T
    Clue: Sport

3. 9 = P in our S S
    Clue: Astronomy

4. 88 = K on a P
    Clue: Music

5. 18 = H on a G C
    Clue: Bunker

6. 90 = D in a R A
    Clue: Geometry

7. 4 = S on a MB
    Clue: Popular game

8. 3 = B M
    Clue: Farmer's Wife

9. 24 = H in a D
    Clue: Time

10. 29 = D in F in a L Y
    Clue: Calendar

SOLUTIONS

1. 12 Signs of the Zodiac. 2. 11 Players in a Football Team.
3. 9 Planets in our Solar System. 4. 88 Keys on a Piano.
5. 18 Holes on a Golf Course. 6. 90 Degrees in a Right Angle.
7. 4 Stations on a Monopoly Board. 8. 3 Blind Mice.
9. 24 Hours in a Day. 10. 29 Days in February in a Leap Year.

A PIECE OF CAKE
The Professor's Birthday

The university professors are having a birthday party and they take the opportunity to test Trevor's cleverness. Trevor must cut a birthday cake into exactly eight pieces, but he's allowed to make only three straight cuts, and he isn't allowed to move pieces of the cake as he cuts it. How can he do it?

SOLUTION

Trevor uses the first two cuts to cut an 'X' in the top of the cake. Now he has four pieces. He makes the third cut horizontally through the cake, dividing the four pieces into eight. Now there are four pieces on the top tier and four more underneath it.

DAFFYNITIONS
To Absurd Words

The answers to these word definitions are all a bit silly. Bear that in mind while you're looking for the answers!

1. What do you call a person who studies contented parrots?

2. What do you call a crate of ducks?

3. What do you call a dentist in Scotland?

4. What is the term for a line of rabbits hopping backwards?

5. What is the term for a cow with very short legs?

6. What word means someone who is afraid of Santa?

7. What do you call cheese that belongs to someone else?

8. What do you call crocodile photographs?

9. What is the proper term for a camel with three humps?

10. What is artificial pasta also known as?

11. What do you call a boomerang that flies straight?

12. What do you call a man who keeps rabbits?

13. What word describes a television study about sheep?

14. What do you call a person who poisons corn flakes?

15. What do you call a Russian 'flu specialist?

16. What term describes a tramp with abnormally short legs?

17. What do you call a cow with no sense of direction?

18. What is a group of flying rabbits known as?

19. What are parallel rows of vegetables also called?

20. What do you call a fly that has no wings?

21. What do you call a person that collects wild mushrooms?

22. What is the "laughing lizard" also called?

23. What do you call a country where everybody has a pink car?

24. What do you call a man who studies dead leaves?

25. What game do elephants like to play most?

SOLUTIONS

1. A jollypollyologist! 2. A box of quackers! 3. Phil McCavity! 4. A receding Hare line! 5. Ground Beef! 6. Clausterphobic! 7. Nacho Cheese! 8. Snapshots! 9. Humphrey! 10. Mockaroni! 11. A stick! 12. Warren! 13. Flockumentary! 14. A cereal killer! 15. Ivan Ortulkoff! 16. A low down bum! 17. Udderly lost! 18. The hare force! 19. A dual cabbageway! 20. A walk! 21. A fungi to be with! 22. A stand-up chameleon! 23. A pink carnation! 24. Russell! 25. Squash!

FIGURE IT OUT

Mathematical Puzzles

1. Two men were talking about their families. "How many kids do you have?" Mr. Brown asked Mr. White. "I have three," Mr. White replied. "What are their ages?" asked Mr. Brown. Mr. White answered, "Let's see how good your maths is. Multiply their three ages and you get 36, add their three ages and you get 13, and two of them are twins." Mr. Brown thought for a moment, and then said, "My maths is pretty good, but I get two possible answers." "My oldest child is a girl," said Mr. White. Then Mr. Brown was able to come up with the correct answer. Can you?

2. What is the significance of the following date and time? The year is 1978, thirty-four minutes past noon on June 5th.

3. You have 9 marbles, 8 that weigh 1 ounce each, and 1 that weighs 1.1 ounces. The marbles are all the same size and look identical. You have a set of scales that contains 2 trays. You are able to use the scale only twice. How do you work out which marble is the heaviest?

SOLUTIONS

1. The only two sets of three numbers that multiply together to make 36 and add up to 13 are 9, 2, 2 and 6, 6, 1. Mr. Brown knew that 9, 2, 2 was the correct set when he found out that the single child was older than the two twins.

2. The time and month/date/year are 12:34, 5/6/78.

3. Place 3 marbles on each tray. If the scales don't balance, place one marble on each tray from the heavier tray. The heavier side now is the 1.1 ounce marble, unless they balance, then the 3rd marble from the heavier ounce tray is the 1.1 ounce marble. If the marbles balance the first time, place any 2 of the remaining unweighed marbles on the trays, one on each tray. If one is heavier, it is the heavier marble (1.1 ounces), but if they balance, the remaining unweighed marble is the heavier one!

A BRIDGE TOO FAR

A too tall story

There is a low bridge just outside your town. One day you see a large truck stopped just before the underpass. When you ask what has happened, the driver tells you that his truck is one inch higher than the indicated height of the bridge. This is the only road he can use to get to his destination. What can he do to get through the underpass the easiest way?

SOLUTION

Let enough air out of the tyres to lower the truck.

WRITE STUFF
Word Puzzles & Teasers

All these sets of words can become new words by placing the same common word AFTER them. For example:

out, set, draw, cut

can become new words or phrases by placing the word BACK after them: outBACK, setBACK, drawBACK, cutBACK

Now see if you can find the word that goes after the following:

1. foot, net, hand, base *ball*
2. sea, race, hobby, rocking *horse*
3. sports, street, side, saloon *car*
4. tap, mineral, flood, dish *water*
5. forest, back, spit, wild *fire*
6. ever, bowling, pea, sea *green*
7. polar, teddy, grizzly, brown *bear*
8. hand, telephone, note, text *book*
9. air, pass, trans, sea *port*
10. den, book, hall, land *mark*
11. dry, fin, main, high *land*
12. green, hot, ware, club *house*
13. sit, write, show, shut *down*
14. gold, lock, black, hammer *smith*
15. sleep, moon, space, side *walk*
16. hot, hammer, fore, over *head*
17. out, in, next, open *door*
18. home, house, fire, team *work*
19. high, sun, night, spot *light*
20. gear, post, ice, juke. *box*

SOLUTIONS

1. BALL. 2. HORSE. 3. CAR. 4. WATER. 5. FIRE. 6. GREEN. 7. BEAR. 8. BOOK. 9. PORT. 10. MARK. 11. LAND. 12. HOUSE. 13. DOWN. 14. SMITH. 15. WALK. 16. HEAD. 17. DOOR. 18. WORK. 19. LIGHT. 20. BOX.

DOUBLE DUTCH
Codes & Ciphers

1.

This is a "cryptogram" — a straight-forward substitition code, where each letter of the alphabet has been substituted for another. The words are still in their correct order, with a space between each. Start your decoding by looking for small, common words like THE, AND, TO and A. Replace each letter with the correct one to crack the code and reveal an amusing quotation...

RTVY HYTHNY RCF KE'R JYEEYG ET JY
HTTG CDB WCHHF EWCD GKUW CDB
VKRYGCJNY; K'B RYEENY ZTG
VTBYGCEYNF GKUW CDB VTTBF

2.

Another cryptogram, this time to reveal a quotation from legendary scientist Albert Einstein. Again the cryptogram is in a straightforward substitution code where each letter of the alphabet has been substituted for another.

MEH GMMHIVM MB KBIQOPH AOCZBI
GPZ VBAHT EGC BPRN TGTHRN QHHP
CLKKHCCYLR GPZ MEHP BPRN YBT G
CEBTM AEORH.

General Riddles

1. What is the smallest number of cars that can be driven in this formation: two cars in front of a car, two cars behind a car, and a car between two cars?

2. A tramp who collects cigar butts can make a cigar to smoke out of every 5 butts that he finds. Today, he has collected 25 cigar butts.
How many cigars will he be able to smoke?

3. Someone at a party introduces you to your mother's only sister's husband's sister-in-law. He has no brothers.
What is this lady to you?

4. If you start with the number one and use only whole numbers, how far do you have to count before you need to use the letter "a" in spelling out a number?

5. This sentense contains two mistakes. What are the mistakes?

6. Mr. and Mrs. Smith have six daughters and each daughter has one brother.
How many people in the family?

SOLUTIONS

1. Three: one car in front, one in the middle, and one behind.
2. Six, he makes 5 originals from the 25 butts he found, and after he smokes them he has 5 butts left to make another cigar.
3. She's your mum! 4. One thousand.
5. First mistake: the second "s" in the word "sentense" should be a "c".
Second mistake: there is only one mistake in the sentence.
6. There are 9 family members in total: 6 daughters, 1 brother, Mr. Smith and Mrs. Smith.

BOBBY's WORLD
What's the Secret?

You're in a place called "Bobby's World"
and there is only one law.
There is a mirror, but no reflection.
There is pizza with cheese,
but not sausage.
There is pepper, but no salt.
There is a door, yet no entrance or exit.

So what is the law in Bobby's world?

SOLUTION

Everything in Bobby's world must contain double letters in each word.

PIC & MIX
Silly Word Puzzles

1. What do you get if you cross a pig with a nudist?

2. What do you get if you cross a jogger with an apple pie?

3. What do you get if you cross a computer with a potato?

4. What do you get if you cross a motorcycle and a funny story?

5. What do you get if you cross a sheep and a space ship?

6. What do you get if you cross two bees and a coach?

7. What do you get if you cross a carrier pigeon with a woodpecker?

8. What do you get if you cross a cat with a parrot?

9. What do you get if you cross a cake and a disco?

10. What do you get if you cross a dinosaur with a dog?

11. What do you get if you cross a mouse and a bottle of olive oil?

12. What do you get if you cross a bunch of flowers with a burglar?

13. What do you get if you cross a leopard and a bunch of flowers?

14. What do you get if you cross a book and a pound of fat?

15. What do you get if you cross a fish and a Ducati?

16. What do you get if you cross a pig and an emergency vehicle?

17. What do you get if you cross a pig and a telephone?

18. What do you get if you cross a vampire and a plumber?

19. What do you get if you cross a vampire and a mummy?

20. What do you get if you cross a bike and a rose?

21. What do you get if you cross a skunk with a boomerang?

22. What is the largest ant in the world?

23. What do you get if you cross a cow with a crystal ball?

24. What do you get if you cross a bear with a skunk?

25. What do you get when you cross a cow and a duck?

SOLUTIONS

1. Streaky bacon! 2. Puff pastry! 3. Micro chips! 4. A Yamahahaha! 5. Apollo neck jumpers! 6. A double decker buzz! 7. A bird that knocks before delivering the post! 8. A carrot! 9. Abundance! 10. Tyrannosaurus Rex! 11. A squeak that oils itself! 12. Robbery with violets! 13. A beauty spot! 14. Lard of the rings! 15. A motor pike! 16. A hambulance! 17. A lot of crackling on the line! 18. A drain in the neck! 19. Something you wouldn't want to unwrap! 20. Bicycle petals! 21. A horrendous smell that keeps coming back! 22. ElephANT! 23. A message from the udder side! 24. Winnie-the-Pooh! 25. Cheese and quackers!

WRITE STUFF
Word Puzzles & Teasers

Can you fill in the blanks to complete the following unusual-looking words?

1. ??thom

2. ?wkw???

3. ?athem?????

4. ??oela??

5. ?ylop????

6. ??epher?

7. ?illili???

8. ??ayg?????

9. ?ewil???

10. i?l?o

11. ???mert???

12. ???drob?

13. ????guta?

14. ????momet??

15. ??rtoi??

SOLUTIONS

1. fathom. 2. awkward. 3. mathematics. 4. shoelace. 5. xylophone. 6. shepherd. 7. millilitre. 8. playground. 9. bewilder. 10. igloo. 11. summertime. 12. wardrobe. 13. orangutan. 14. thermometer. 15. tortoise.

HOW CANOE DO THAT?
The Wolf, the Hen and the Grain

You are at a river. With you are a chicken, a bag of grain, and a wolf.
You have to cross the river in your canoe but can take only one with you at a time.
You can't leave the chicken with the grain. He'll eat it. You can't leave the wolf with the chicken. He'll eat it.
How do you get everything over and intact?

SOLUTION

Take the chicken over first and leave it on the other side. Next, take the wolf across and leave him, but bring the chicken back with you. Next trip, leave the chicken where you started and take the grain across. Leave it on the other side with the wolf. Finally, go back and get the chicken.

WHO DUNNIT

Crime Puzzles

1. Old Mr Tidy was found dead in his study by Mr Fiend. Mr Fiend recounted his dismal discovery to the police.
"I was walking by Mr Tidy's house when I thought I would just pop in for a visit. I noticed his study light was on and I decided to peek in from the outside to see if he was in there. There was condensation on the window, so I had to wipe it away to see inside. That is when I saw his body. So I kicked in the front door to confirm my suspicions of foul play. I called the police immediately afterwards."
The officer immediately arrested Mr Fiend for the murder of Mr Tidy. How did he know Mr Fiend was lying?

2. A man has been murdered. He is hanging by a rope in a completely empty room. The floor is wet. How did the murderers claim their victim?

3. A man was found dead out in a field of snow. The only tracks that were left was a set of footprints between two parallel lines. Who should the police be looking for?

SOLUTIONS

1. Condensation forms on the inside of the window, not the outside. So Mr. Fiend could not have wiped it off to discover Mr. Tidy's body.
2. They stood the man on top of a large block of ice which has now melted.
3. A man in a wheelchair.

WORDOODLES
Say what you see

Each of these Wordoodles is a word,
phrase or saying, cunningly disguised!
For example:
"minI'LL BE THEREute"
Would mean: "I'll be there in a minute!"
See how you get on with these...

1. Give Get Give Get
   Give Get Give Get

2. ooodomooo

3.   mad
   mad U mad
      mad

4.   A P
   E   P
   S   L
    U A

5.   r
     o
   roads
     d
     s

6. hahandnd

7. noon good

8. SGEG

9. b
   bow
    w

SOLUTIONS

1. Forgive and Forget (Four give and Four get). 2. Dominoes.
3. Mad about you. 4. Round of applause. 5. Crossroads. 6. Hand in hand.
7. Good afternoon. 8. Scrambled eggs. 9. Crossbow.

21

FIRST CLASS CARNAGE!

Murder in the Mountains

The midnight train is rattling down the mountains. Art Farnanski appears to be dozing off in his seat, but someone knows that this is not the case.
At the station, all the passengers get off the train, except one, of course.
The conductor comes and taps him on the shoulder to let him know
that they have arrived at their destination.
Art Farnanski does not answer.
He is dead.

Hours later the four people that had shared the train compartment with the dead man are at the police station.

The man in the dark suit:
"I'm innocent.
The blonde woman was talking to Farnanski."

The blonde woman:
"I'm innocent.
I did not speak to Farnanski."

The man in the light suit:
"I'm innocent.
The brunette woman killed him."

The brunette woman:
"I'm innocent.
One of the men killed him."

That same morning, while he is serving him coffee, the waiter at the Petit Piccolo asks the Police Commander,
"This is an easy case for you isn't it?"

FIRST CLASS CARNAGE!

Murder in the Mountains

"Yes," answers the commander. "Four suspects, four true statements and four false ones. Easy as pie."

Who killed Farnanski?
(Only one person is guilty).

SOLUTION

The blonde woman killed Mr Farnanski. There are only four true statements. Only one person is guilty. Therefore, three of the "I'm innocent" statements are true. Only one more statement can be true, and this must be the one made by the man in the dark suit or by the blonde woman. Therefore, "The brunette killed him" and "One of the men killed him" are false statements, so the blonde woman is the killer!

MATCH OF THE DAY
Matchstick Puzzles

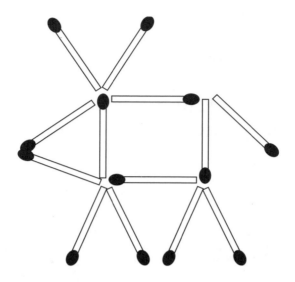

Rudolph the match reindeer is looking
to the left. Can you make him look the other
way by moving just 2 of the matches?

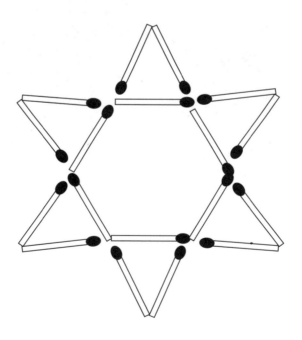

There are 8 triangles in this 6-pointed star.
Can you reposition 2 matches to make a
6-pointed star with only 6 visible triangles?

Answers on page 157

FIGURE IT OUT
Mathematical Puzzles

1. Amoebas reproduce by splitting in two. An amoeba which does this once every minute is placed in a jar at exactly ten o'clock in the morning.
At 12:00 noon the jar is full.
At what time is the jar half full?

2. A frog fell into a well that was 12 feet deep. He could jump 3 feet, but every time he did, he would fall back 2 feet. How many times did the frog have to jump until he got out of the well?

3. The stubs obtained by burning ten candles will make one extra candle if you melt them all together.
If you burned 100 candles, how many extra candles could you make?

4. King Tut died 120 years after King Eros was born. Their combined ages when they died was 100 years.
King Eros died in the year 40 B.C.
In what year was King Tut born?

5. There is a cage at the zoo that contains both peacocks and pigs. If there is a total of 30 eyes and 44 feet, how many of each are there in the cage?

SOLUTIONS

1. 11:59am 2. Ten. On the 10th jump he reached 13 feet and got out. 3. Eleven. The 10 extra from the 100 candles, and then one more from burning the extra 10 stubs you have. 4. He was born 20 B.C. There were 120 years between the birth of King Eros and the death of King Tut, but since their ages amounted to 100 years, there must have been 20 years when neither existed. This would be the period between the death of King Eros, 40 B.C and the birth of King Tut, 20 B.C. 5. Seven pigs and eight peacocks.

WHAT AM I?

Mystery Objects

1. Forward I'm heavy,
Backward I'm not.
What am I?

2. We're five little items of an everyday
sort: you'll find us all in a tennis court.
What are we?

3. You use me between your head and
your toes, the more I works the thinner I
grows. What am I?

4. I dig out tiny caves, and store gold and
silver in them. I also build bridges of
silver and make crowns of gold. They are
the smallest you could imagine. Sooner or
later everybody needs my help, yet many
people are afraid to let me help them.
Who am I?

5. I know what my job is, the point has
been made. You say I have a big head,
and you're right, I'm afraid. Put me in my
place, and then leave me alone. What I
need most is someone to drive me home.
What am I?

6. I am a word of five letters.
If you take away the first and last letters,
I will still sound the same.
Even if you take the middle letter,
I will be the same as before.
What am I?

SOLUTIONS

1. A ton. 2. The vowels in order (A tEnnis cOUrt). 3. A bar of soap.
4. A dentist. 5. A nail 6. Empty.

HAIR OR THERE
A Traveller's Tale

A traveller arrives in a small town and decides he wants to get a haircut. According to the manager of the hotel where he's staying, there are only two barber shops in town - one on East Street and one on West Street. The traveller goes to check out both shops. The East Street barber shop is a mess, and the barber has the worst haircut the traveller has ever seen. The West Street barber shop is neat and clean; its barber's hair looks as good as a movie star's. Which barber shop does the traveller go to for his haircut, and why?

SOLUTION

The traveller goes to have his hair cut at the barber shop on East Street. He figures that since there are only two barber shops in town, the East Street barber must have his hair cut by the West Street barber and vice versa. So if the traveller wants to look as good as the West Street barber (the one with the good haircut), he'd better go to the man who cuts it. Also he figures, the reason the West Street barber shop is so clean and neat is that it seldom gets any customers.

SAY SOMETHING STUPID
Silly Riddles

1. Take away my first letter and I remain the same. Take away my second letter and I remain unchanged. Take away my third letter and I am unchanged. Take away all my letters and I am still exactly the same. What am I?

2. In Okmulgee, Oklahoma, you cannot take a picture of a man with a wooden leg. Why not?

3. What goes up and down the stairs without moving?

4. The assistant in the fishmonger's is 5 feet 10 inches tall. What does he weigh?

5. What kind of room has no windows or doors?

6. A barrel of water weighs 20 pounds. What must you add to it to make it weigh 12 pounds?

7. What is the biggest building in the world?

8. What kind of rocks are on the bottom of the Mississippi River?

9. What starts with a T, ends with a T, and has T in it?

10. What two words contain the most letters?

11. What's the greatest worldwide use of cowhide?

12. Which moves faster: heat or cold?

13. A young man is trapped inside a solid steel room with 10-foot-thick walls. There is only one steel door which is locked. There are no windows and no skylight.
However, the young man does have a baseball and bat. How does he get out?

14. Who's bigger: Mr Bigger, Mrs Bigger or their baby?

15. When the SS Pietanic sank, every single person on board the ship died, yet two people survived.
How is this possible?

16. A railroad crossing, look for the cars; Can you spell all that without any R's?

17. How can you lift an adult elephant with one hand?

18. And what do you get if you cross a mountain and a baby?

SOLUTIONS

18. A cry for Alp!
17. You can't. Elephants don't have hands!
15. They weren't single, they were married! 16. All that.
14. The baby, because he's a little bigger!
13. He takes the baseball bat, throws the ball up in the air three times, swings with the bat and misses each time. Three strikes and he's out!
12. Heat. (Everybody can catch a cold!)
10. Post office! 11. To hold cows together!
7. A library, because it has the most stories! 8. Wet rocks! 9. A teapot!
wooden leg! 3. A carpet! 4. Fish! 5. Mushrooms! 6. Holes!
1. A postman! 2. Because you need a camera to take a picture, not a

LUCKY DIP
General Riddles

1. With a little thought, the following facts can make an accurate statement. Can you figure it out?
111 is a race horse, 112 is 12,
11111 race, 112112

2. Steve and Sally where sitting in their front room one night. While Steve was watching T.V. his wife Sally was reading. All of a sudden the power cut out and Steve decided to go to bed, but Sally kept on reading. With no use of artificial light, Sally finished her book. How?

3. Think of words ending in -GRY. Angry and hungry are two of them. There are only three words in the English language. What is the third word? The word is something that everyone uses every day. If you have read carefully, I have already told you what it is.

4. Two men were drinking in a pub. Two women walked in. The first man said, "I have to go, my wife and daughter are here." The second man turned around and said, "I have to go too, my wife and daughter just arrived as well." How is this possible?

SOLUTIONS

1. One One One is a race horse, One One Two is one too One One One won one race, One One Two won one too.
2. Sally was blind... she was reading a book by Braille.
3. The key sentences are
"There are only three words in "The English language".
What is the third word? The third word is "language".
4. The two men in question were both divorced with a daughter from a previous marriage. They both married the other's daughter.

30

HELP, POLICE!

A Cop on the Case

A cop was walking past a restaurant when he heard someone scream - "No John, not the gun!" He ran inside and and saw a doctor, a lawyer, a milkman, and a dead body on the floor. He promptly walked over to the milkman and arrested him. He didn't witness the shooting, there was no apparent evidence to prove who shot the person, and no one told him who the killer was. How did the policeman instantly know it was the milkman?

SOLUTION

The milkman was the only male present. The doctor and lawyer were females, so the cop knew that "John" was the milkman.

STUPID ANSWERS
To sensible questions

1. Why do sea-gulls fly over the sea?

2. Why do so few dogs visit psychiatrists?

3. Why are giraffes' necks so long?

4. Why should you never buy dogs that are going cheap?

5. Why can't a leopard hide?

SOLUTIONS

1. Because if they flew over the bay they would be bagels!
2. Because they're not allowed on the couch!
3. Because their feet stink!
4. Because a healthy dog should go "Woof!"
5. Because he's always spotted!

KING CON!
The Two Marbles

On his birthday, a king was supposed to let a prisoner try to escape his prison with his life. The king was to place two marbles in a jar that was glued to a table. One of the marbles was supposed to be black, and one was supposed to be blue.

If the prisoner could pick the blue marble, he would escape the prison with his life. If he picked the black marble, he would be executed. However, the king was very mean, and he wickedly placed two black marbles in the jars and no blue marbles!

KING CON!

The Two Marbles

Now, the prisoner SAW the king putting
only two black marbles in the jars, and
realised the pickle he was in.
How did he escape with his life, knowing
that there were two black marbles
in the jar?

SOLUTION

The prisoner grabbed one of the marbles from the jar and concealed it in his
hand. He then swallowed it, and picked up the other marble and showed
everyone. The marble was black, and since the other marble was
swallowed, it was assumed to be the blue one. So the mean king had to
set him free.

What's a Droodle? Well, a Droodle is a doodle that's drawn of something from a strange angle, so you can't really tell what it is. So this picture below is ... a goal! Seen from the back, obviously!

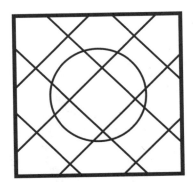

So now you've the idea, let's have a look at one that's a little more complicated. The droodle below is of a Viking wash-day...

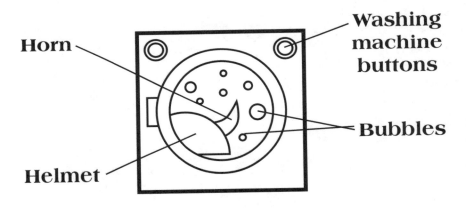

You see now?

OK, so what are the droodles on the opposite page?

DROODLES
Picture Puzzles

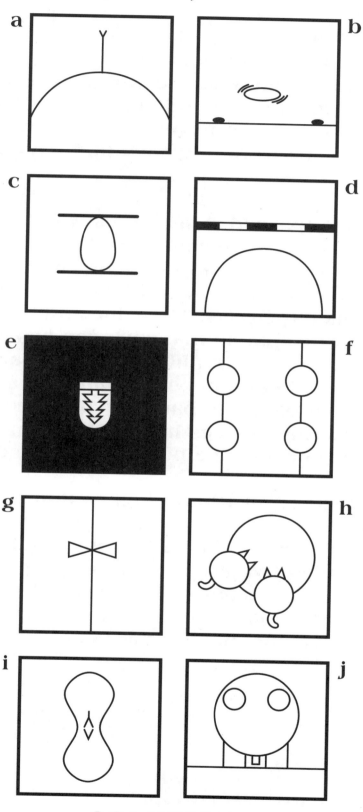

SOLUTIONS

i. Duck yawning. j. Elephant doing a hand stand.
f. Bear climbing a tree. g. Bow tie in lift. h. Two cats drinking milk.
c. Egg sandwich. d. Bald limbo-dancer. e. Bat's view from cave.
a. Almost bald man's split end. b. Ants playing frisbee.

35

FIGURE IT OUT
Mathematical Puzzles

1. Joe bought a bag of oranges on Monday, and ate a third of them. On Tuesday he ate half of the remaining oranges. On Wednesday he looked in the bag to find he only had two oranges left. How many oranges were originally in the bag?

2. The 99-year-old owner of a winery recently passed away. In his will, he left 21 beautiful rosewood barrels - seven of which are filled with wine, seven of which are half full, and seven of which are empty - to his three sons. The wine and barrels must be split so that each son has the same number of full barrels, the same number of half-full barrels, and the same number of empty barrels. There are no measuring devices handy. How can the barrels and wine be evenly divided?

3. You have a 12-litre jug, an 8-litre jug, and a 5-litre jug. None of the jugs has any markings on it. The 12-litre jug is full, and the other two are empty. How can you divide the 12 litres of water equally, so two of the jugs have exactly 6 litres of water in them, and the third one is empty?

SOLUTIONS

1. He had 6 oranges to start with, and ate 2 the first day and 2 the second day. 2. Two half-full barrels are poured into one of the empty barrels. Two more half-full barrels are poured into another one of the empty barrels. This results in nine full barrels, three half-full barrels, and nine empty barrels. Each son gets three full barrels, one half-full barrel, and three empty barrels.
3. Fill the 5-litre jug using the 8-litre jug, leaving 3 litres.
Fill the 5-litre jug using the 8-litre jug, leaving 4 litres.
Empty the 5-litre jug into the 12-litre jug.
Now there are 9 litres in the 12-litre jug and 3 in the 8-litre jug. Pour the 3 litres from the 8-litre jug into the 5-litre jug. Now fill the 8-litre jug with water from the 12-litre jug, leaving 1 litre in the 12-litre jug.
Fill the 5-litre jug (which already has 3 litres in it) from the 8-litre jug, leaving 6 litres in the 8-litre jug. Empty the 5-litre jug into the 12-litre jug.
Now there are 6 litres in the 12-litre jug, 6 litres in the 8-litre jug, and the 5-litre jug is empty!

LETTUCE PRAY!

The Rabbit's Lunch

Raoul the Rabbit was starving! He came to a farmer's lettuce garden but it was surrounded by a picket fence. Raoul knew he must eat soon or he would die! He could barely fit through the fence in his present condition and he knew that if he entered and ate the lettuce he would be too fat to fit back through the fence. If the farmer happened to come by he couldn't escape. The lettuce was too big to fit through the fence. How could Raoul eat the lettuce and still manage to escape if the need arose?

SOLUTION

Raoul crawled through the fence and brought the lettuce back to the hole in the fence. He squeezed back through the hole and ate the lettuce from the other side.

DUMB & DUMBER

How stupid do you feel?

This is a selection of tricky riddles that might make you feel stupid when you hear the answers!

1. Why is it against the law for a man living in Scotland to be buried in Wales?

2. The Mississippi River is the dividing line between the American states of Tennessee and Arkansas. If an aeroplane crashed exactly in the middle of the Mississippi River there, where would the survivors be buried?

3. How much dirt would be in a hole 6 feet deep and 6 feet wide that has been dug with a square-edged shovel?

4. If a farmer has 5 haystacks in one field and 4 haystacks in another field, how many haystacks would he have if he combined them all in a third field?

5. In the Bible, how many of each kind of animal did Moses take on board the Ark during the Flood?

6. If it takes 3 people to dig a hole, how many does it take to dig half a hole?

7. What can you sit on, sleep on, and brush your teeth with?

8. Some months have 30 days and some have 31. How many months have 28 days?

9. Clara Clatter was born on December 27th, yet her birthday is always in the summer. How can this be?

10. Before Mount Everest was discovered, what was the tallest mountain in the world?

11. Which weighs more, a pound of feathers or a pound of lead?

12. Two planes take off at the same exact moment. They are flying across the Atlantic. One leaves New York and is flying to Paris at 500 miles per hour. The other leaves Paris and is flying to New York at only 450 miles per hour. Which one will be closer to Paris when they pass each other?

13. Johnny's mother had three children. The first child was named April. The second child was named May. What was the third child's name?

14. If there are 5 apples on the counter and you take away 2, how many do you have?

15. Is it legal for a man in California to marry his widow's sister?

SOLUTIONS

1. Because he is still alive! 2. Nowhere! You don't bury survivors!
3. None. It's a hole, there's nothing in it!
4. One. If you combines 9 haystacks, you get one big haystack!
5. None. Moses didn't take animals on the ark, Noah did!
6. You can't dig half a hole! 7. A chair, a bed and a toothbrush!
8. All of them! 9. She's Australian, December is summer down there!
10. Mount Everest. It was the tallest mountain even before it was discovered!
11. They weigh the same. A pound is a pound!
12. They will be exactly the same distance from Paris when they pass each other!
13. If Johnny's mum had three children, the third one must be Johnny!
14. You have 2 apples. There are 3 left on the counter, but you have 2!
15. No it's not legal. If he has a widow, that means the man is dead!

39

MISSION IMPOSSIBLE
Solving the unsolvable

1. You have a bag with four chocolate bars in it. You promised to give each of your three friends a bar, and you want one for yourself. How can you accomplish this, and still have one bar left in the bag?

2. One day, two mothers and two daughters went shopping for shoes. Their shopping spree was successful - each bought a pair of shoes, and all together, they had three pairs. How is this possible?

3. A man rides into town on Friday. He stays three nights and leaves on Friday.

4. A man was born in 1955. He's alive and well today at age 33. How is this possible?

5. One day Kerry celebrated her birthday. One day later her older twin brother, Terry, celebrated his birthday. Why?

6. Two babies were born on the same day with the same mother and father but are not twins.

SOLUTIONS

1. Give each friend a chocolate bar and keep the chocolate bar in the bag for yourself! 2. Only three people went shopping: a grandmother, a mother, and a daughter - but remember that the mother was the grandmother's daughter! 3. Friday is a horse! 4. He was born in the hospital, in room number 1955! 5. At the time she went into labour, the mother of the twins was travelling by boat. The older twin, Terry, was born first, early on March 1st. The boat then crossed the International Date Line, and Kerry, the younger twin, was born on February 28th. Therefore, the younger twin celebrates her birthday one day before her older brother. 6. The two babies are two of a set of triplets.

MULE BE SORRY!
The Salt and the Donkey

Every day, Tom tied two sacks of salt to the back of his donkey and headed to market to sell it. On the way, they passed a stream, and one day, the donkey jumped in to cool himself. As a result, a lot of the salt dissolved into the water, ruining the salt for Tom, but making the donkey's load a lot lighter!
The donkey got wise to this and the following day he jumped in the stream again, and the next day, and the next!

Tom knew he had to teach the donkey a new lesson, but what could he do to make sure the donkey stayed out of the water in future?

SOLUTION

Tom must load the sacks not with salt but with sponges. When the donkey jumps in the stream and gets the sacks wet, they'll get heavier!

APPLIANCE OF SCIENCE
Scientific Puzzles

1. Hanging over a pulley is a rope with a weight at one end. At the other end clings a monkey, of equal weight. What do you think will happen if the monkey begins climbing the rope? (You can ignore the weight of the rope and pulley, and assume the pulley is frictionless.)

2. Why is it better to have round manhole covers than square ones?

3. A man went to a party and drank a glass of punch, then left early. Everyone else at the party who drank the punch subsequently died of poisoning. Why did the man not die?

4. You have two cups, one containing orange juice and one containing and equal amount of lemonade. One teaspoon of the orange juice is taken and mixed with the lemonade. Then a teaspoon of this mixture is mixed back into the orange juice. Is there more lemonade in the orange juice or more orange juice in the lemonade?

5. A man has two eggs. One is raw and the other is boiled. He would like to eat the boiled egg for lunch and save the raw one to have for breakfast the next morning. How can he find the boiled egg without breaking the wrong egg by mistake?

APPLIANCE OF SCIENCE
Scientific Puzzles

6. Why would it take a plane flying from New York to London non-stop longer than the same plane flying from London to New York, when the weather, speed, winds, and other flying conditions are the same each way?

7. A person in a boat on a swimming pool drops a cannonball overboard; does the water level change? How?

8. There is a barrel with no lid and some wine in it. "This barrel of wine is more than half full," said Curly. Moe says, "No it's not. It's less than half full." Without any measuring implements and without removing any wine from the barrel, how can they easily determine who is correct?

SOLUTIONS

8. Tilt the barrel until the wine touches the lip of the barrel. If the bottom of the barrel is visible then it is less than half full. If the barrel bottom is still covered by the wine, then it is more than half full.

7. The cannonball in the boat displaces an amount of water equal to the MASS of the cannonball. The cannonball in the water displaces an amount of water equal to the VOLUME of the cannonball. Water isn't as heavy as iron, so the first amount will be more than the second amount, and the water level will drop.

6. The earth rotates from west to east, so the plane would have to fly farther to get to New York.

5. If the man spins the eggs on a flat surface, the hardboiled egg will spin more smoothly than the raw egg. Raw eggs wobble when spun.

4. There's exactly the same amount of lemonade in the orange juice as orange juice in the lemonade. Each cup ends with the same volume of liquid that it started with, and there's still an equal amount of each juice between the two cups.

3. The poison was in the ice cubes and they hadn't melted yet when he drank from the punch.

2. A square manhole cover can be turned and dropped diagonally down the manhole. A round manhole can't. So for safety and practicality, all manhole covers should be round.

1. If the monkey pulls down on the rope hard enough to pull itself up, this will increase the tension in the rope just enough to cause the weight to rise at the same rate as the monkey.

43

PANTS ON FIRE!
Who's telling the truth?

1. How quickly can you find out what is so unusual about this paragraph? It looks so ordinary that you would think that nothing is wrong with it at all, and, in fact, nothing is. But it is unusual. Why? If you study it and think about it, you may find out, but I am not going to assist you in any way. You must do it without coaching. No doubt, if you work at it for long, it will dawn on you. Who knows? Go to work and try your skill. Par is about half an hour.

2. Alice is walking one day through the forest of forgetfulness. She wants to know what day of the week it is.
She stops and asks a passing lion and his friend, a unicorn.
Now the lion lies all of the time on Monday, Tuesday, and Wednesday.
The unicorn always lies on Thursday, Friday and Saturday.
Alice decides to ask the lion what day it is. He says,
"Well, yesterday was one of my lying days." Then she asks the unicorn and the unicorn says, "Yesterday was also one of my lying days."
Can Alice work out from the lion's and unicorn's statements what day it is?

SOLUTIONS

1. The letter 'e' does not appear in the paragraph. 2. Yes, it's Thursday.

44

ROCKS AND LOCKS
The Sultan's Dilemma

The Sultan of Spanooli wants to send a huge diamond to his brother in the mail and he is worried about someone finding and stealing it before it reaches its destination. He has a box which can be fitted with two locks, and he has lots of padlocks and their keys. However, his brother does not have the keys to the Sultan's locks. How can he send the diamond securely locked, and still allow his brother to open the box?

SOLUTION

The Sultan puts the diamond into the box, secures it with one of his locks, and sends the box to his brother. His brother then attaches one of his own locks and returns it. When the Sultan gets the box back, he removes his lock, and sends it back to his brother.

WRITE STUFF
Word Puzzles & Teasers

All these sets of words can become new words by placing a common word IN FRONT of them. For example:

like, long, jacket, line

can become new words by placing the word LIFE in front:
LIFElike, LIFElong, LIFEjacket, LIFEline

Now see if you can find the word that goes before the following:

1. strings, throb, break, burn.
2. out, list, mail, board.
3. charge, board, all, cast.
4. paper, pit, stone, storm.
5. right, cat, writer, book.
6. grade, pour, fall, stream.
7. stool, step, loose, hill.
8. coming, bread, hand, fall.
9. cast, minded, band, bean.
10. day, set, beam, stroke.
11. chant, ding, pal, knife.
12. man, head, told, most.
13. day, right, place, mark.
14. salt, son, side, shore.
15. give, get, tune, mat.
16. due, lap, arm, coat.
17. let, leader, road, tone.
18. fly, man, works, place.
19. ball, storm, drift, man.
20. fall, works, ski, mark.

SOLUTIONS

1. HEART. 2. BLACK. 3. OVER. 4. SAND. 5. COPY. 6. DOWN. 7. FOOT. 8. SHORT. 9. BROAD. 10. SUN. 11. PEN. 12. FORE. 13. BIRTH. 14. SEA. 15. FOR. 16. OVER. 17. RING. 18. FIRE. 19. SNOW. 20. WATER

LUCKY DIP
General Riddles

1. Your sock drawer contains twenty white socks and twenty black socks. If you're allowed to take only one sock from the drawer at a time and it's dark, so you can't see what colour sock you're taking until you've taken it, how many socks do you have to take out of the drawer before you're guaranteed to have at least one matching pair?

2. In your bigger sock drawer, you have ten blue socks, eight brown socks, and twelve black socks. In complete darkness again, how many socks would you need to pull out to get a matching pair of the same colour?

3. A word I know,
Six letters it contains,
Subtract just one,
And twelve is what remains.

4. I went into the woods and got it,
I sat down to seek it,
I brought it home with me
because I couldn't find it. What?

5. Two men were playing tennis. They played five sets and each man won three sets. How can this be possible?

SOLUTIONS

1. Three. In the worst case, the first two socks you take out will consist of one black sock and one white sock. The next sock you take out is guaranteed to match one or the other.
2. Four. If you don't agree, try it yourself! 3. Dozens.
4. A splinter. 5. The two men were partners playing doubles.

47

WORDOODLES

Say what you see

Each of these Wordoodles is a word, phrase or saying, cunningly disguised! For example: minI'LL BE THEREute would mean: "I'll be there in a minute!" See how you get on with these...

1. ban ana

2. issue issue
   issue issue
   issue issue
   issue issue
   issue issue

3. nafish
   nafish

4. lookuleap

5. ware
   lacy

6. £0.00 all all all all

7. habirdnd = bu2sh

8. japmadean

9. lo ose

10.   t
    s   u
    i   h
    t   s

SOLUTIONS

1. Banana split. 2. Tennis shoes (Ten Issues). 3. Tuna fish (Two Nafish). 4. Look before you leap. 5. Lacy underwear! 6. Free for all. 7. A bird in the hand is worth two in the bush. 8. Made in Japan. 9. Broken loose. 10. Sit down and shut up!

SAFE AS HOUSES
An Inside Job

A couple that owned a mansion came home from church to find that their safe had been robbed. They gathered all of their hired servants for questioning. The cook was questioned first and she said that she was busy preparing the Sunday dinner. Next was the butler but he said that he was setting the table for the Sunday dinner. Then they questioned the maid and her excuse was that she had been cleaning the dining room along with the butler. So they moved on and asked the gardener and he stated that after finishing the pruning he went to sort the day's post. The couple, stumped by the reasonable alibis, soon found that one of the staff wasn't being entirely truthful. Who was it?

SOLUTION

The gardener is lying: there is no post on Sundays.

FIGURE IT OUT
Mathematical Puzzles

1. Each of the following questions contains a number sequence. Using the options provided, select the number which should come next in the sequence.

1a. **88, 168, 248, 328, 408, ?**

1b. **951, 1951, 950, 1950, 949, ?**

1c. **3, 5, 15, 17, 51, ?**

1d. **6, 14, 18, 28, 30 ?**

1e. **1, 5, 13, 29, 61, ?**

2. When he was a child, Tommy wanted to buy his mother three red roses for her birthday. He decided to start saving on the first day of the month. On the first day, he put one penny in his piggy bank, on the second day he put two pennies, on the third day three pennies and so on. By the day of her birthday, he had saved up three pounds, exactly the correct amount to buy the three red roses. What day of the month was her birthday?

SOLUTIONS

2. The 24th day of the month
1e. 125. Each number in the sequence is doubled, and then has 3 added to it.
1d. 42. Starting from 1, alternate multiplying each number by either 6 or 7, i.e. 1x6, 2x7, 3x6, 4x7, 5x6, 6x7.
1c. 53. Each term in the sequence is given by alternately adding 2 or multiplying by 3.
1b. 1949. Starting from 951, each number in the sequence is given by alternating between adding 1000, or subtracting 1001.
1a. 488. Each term in the sequence has 80 added to it.

MATCH OF THE DAY

Matchstick Puzzles

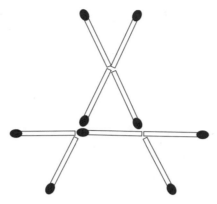

Reposition 4 matches from this pattern
to form 5 triangles.

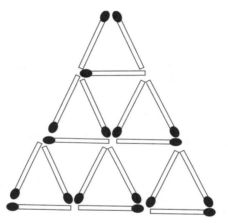

Reposition 6 of the matches in the pattern
above to make 6 equal-sized diamond shapes
in a star pattern.

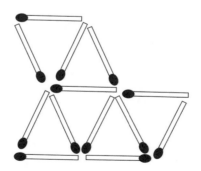

Take away 3 matches from the pattern above
to leave just 3 triangles.

Answers on page 157

General Riddles

1. What do you call your father-in-law's only child's mother-in-law?

2. There is a house with four walls and each wall faces south. There is a window in each wall. A bear walks by one of the windows. What colour is the bear?

3. What can go up a drainpipe down, but can't go down a drainpipe up?

4. What has four legs but only one foot?

5. The maker doesn't want it; the buyer doesn't use it; and the user doesn't see it. What is it?

6. You are walking through a field, and you find something to eat. It doesn't have bones, and it doesn't have meat. You pick it up and put it into your pocket. You take it home and put it on a shelf, but three days later it walks away! What could it be?

7. There are 20 people in an empty, square room. Each person has full sight of the entire room and everyone in it without turning his head or body, or moving in any way (other than the eyes). Where can you place an apple so that all but one person can see it?

SOLUTIONS

1. Mum. 2. White. If all the walls face south, the house is at the North Pole, and the bear, therefore, is a polar bear. 3. An umbrella. 4. A bed. 5. A coffin. 6. It's an egg! 7. Place the apple on one person's head.

SERIAL GRILLER
A Toast Story

Dad is preparing breakfast for his three children - Dan, Ed, and Frank. Each boy wants Dad to toast one slice of bread for him. The toaster is broken and the grill toasts only one side at a time.
It takes exactly one minute to toast one side of a piece of bread. Dad has figured out how to toast three slices on both sides in only three minutes.
How does he do it?

SOLUTION

First minute: Dad toasts Dan's bread on side 1 and Ed's bread on side 1. Then he removes Dan's slice, turns it over, and puts it back in under the grill. He puts Ed's slice aside and puts Frank's bread under the grill.

Second minute: Dad toasts Dan's bread on side 2 and Frank's bread on side 1. He removes both slices, turns Frank's over, and puts it back under the grill. He gives Dan his toast and puts Ed's slice back under the grill.

Third minute: Dad toasts Frank's slice on side 2 and Ed's slice on side 2. Then he serves those slices to Frank and Ed.

WHAT AM I?

Mystery Objects

1. I'm light as a feather, yet the strongest man can't hold me for much more than a minute. What am I?

2. You use a knife to slice my head, and weep beside me when I am dead. What am I?

3. With thieves I consort,
With the vilest, in short,
I'm quite at my ease in depravity;
Yet all divines use me,
And savants can't lose me,
For I am the centre of gravity.
What am I?

4. Pronounced as one letter,
And written with three,
Two letters there are
And two only in me.
I'm double, I'm single,
I'm black, blue, and grey,
I'm read from both ends,
And the same either way.
What am I?

5. I'm where yesterday follows today, and tomorrow's in the middle. What am I?

6. From the beginning of eternity
To the end of time and space
To the beginning of every end
And the end of every place.
What am I?

7. When I am filled, I can point the way. When I am empty, nothing moves me. What am I?

8. My life can be measured in hours;
I serve by being devoured.
Thin, I am quick; fat, I am slow.
Wind is my foe.
What am I?

9. Lighter than what I'm made of,
more of me is hidden than is seen.
What am I?

10. Whoever makes it, tells it not.
Whoever takes it, knows it not. Whoever
knows it, wants it not. What is it?

11. What does man love more than life?
Fear more than death or mortal strife?
What do the poor have,
What do the rich require,
And what do contented men desire?
What does the miser spend,
The spendthrift save,
And all men carry to their grave?

12. What can run but never walks,
has a mouth but never talks,
has a head but never weeps,
has a bed but never sleeps?

13. Often talked of, never seen, ever
coming, never been, daily looked for,
never here, still approaching, coming
near. Thousands for its visit wait, but alas
for their fate, tho' they expect me to
appear, they will never find me here.
What am I?

14. I'm a god, a planet, and I measure
heat. What am I?

SOLUTIONS

1. Breath. 2. An onion. 3. The letter "V". 4. An eye. 5. A dictionary.
6. The letter "e". 7. A glove. 8. A candle. 9. An iceberg.
10. Counterfeit money. 11. Nothing. 12. A river.
13. Tomorrow. 14. Mercury.

LUCKY DIP
General Riddles

1. How many times can you subtract the number 2 from the number 32?

2. What animal has no wings, but yet will fly?

3. Who can shave 25 times a day and still have a beard?

4. What occurs once in a minute, twice in a moment, but never in an hour?

5. What has to be broken before you can use it?

6. What do you throw out when you want to use it, but take in when you don't want to use it?

7. How can a woman living in Yorkshire legally marry three different men, without ever getting a divorce, becoming legally separated or a widow?

8. How can you put nine pigs in four pig pens such that each pen has an odd number of pigs?

9. How can you express the number 100 using six nines and no other digits?

10. What belongs to you, but others use it more than you do?

SOLUTIONS

1. Once. 2. A caterpillar, which will one day be a butterfly. 3. A barber! 4. The letter "M". 5. An egg. 6. An anchor. 7. She's a vicar. 8. Build three pens and put three pigs in each. Then build a fourth pen around the other three. 9. 99+99/99 10. Your name.

SHOP TIL YOU DROP
Bags of Fun

Mr and Mrs Jones were walking home from the shopping mall with their purchases when Mr Jones began to complain that his load was too heavy. Mrs Jones turned to her husband and asked, "Why are you complaining? If you gave me one of your parcels, I would have twice as many as you, and if I gave you just one of mine, we would have equal loads." How many parcels were they each carrying?

SOLUTION

Mr Jones had 5 parcels. Mrs Jones, 7.

NEXT PLEASE!

Complete the sequence

1. This list of letters follows a pattern. Which letter comes next?

A C F J O ?

2. What is the next letter in the following series?

A C F H K M ?

3. What are the last two numbers in this sequence?

8 5 4 9 1 7 6 10 ? ?

4. What are the next two letters in this series, which works only when the letters are capitals?

A E F H I K L M ?

5. Which fruit should come next in this sequence?

Banana, pear, kiwi, tomato, ?
(Choose from: lemon, plum, guava, peach.)

6. What is the last letter needed to complete this sequence?

O T T F F S S E N ?

7. What is the only other letter that fits in the following series:

B C D E I K O X ?

8. What is the next letter in this series?

S M H D W M ?

9. What are the next two letters in the following series and why?

W A T N T L I T F S ? ?

10. What is the next letter in the series of letters with something in common?

B C D E G ?

11 Continue this pattern with the next two numbers:

1 2 3 5 ? ?

12. Each letter below stands for the name of something in a list. All the names are in the correct order. Two more words complete the list. Can you work out what the last two letters should be?

M V E M J S U ? ?

13. What's seventh and last in this list?

M T W T F S ?

14. What's the last letter to complete this list of seven?

H D B S S G ?

SOLUTIONS

1. The next letter is U. The series moves forward by skipping one letter of the alphabet and then two letters and then three and so on.
2. The next letter is P. The given letters progress as follows: Skip 1 letter, skip 2 letters, skip 1 letter, skip 2 letters, skip 1 letter. So the next letter is 2 letters forward, or P.
3. Three and two. The numbers are in alphabetical order: eight, five, four, nine, one, seven, six, ten, three, two.
4. N and T, these being the next two letters made up solely of straight lines.
5. Guava. The second letters of the words are the five vowels in the correct order.
6. The letters are the initials of the numbers one to ten.
7. The letter H. All of the letters in the series flipped vertically look the same.
8. It's Y for Year. It follows second, minute, hour, day, week and month.
9. A and W (and why) - they are the first letters of every word in the sentence.
10. The next letter would be P. They all rhyme.
11. 1+2=3, 2+3=5, 3+5=8, so the next number is 8. 5+8=13, so the 5th number is 13.
12. N for Neptune, and P for Pluto. The names of the nine planets of our Solar System in order from their distance from the Sun.
13. S again, for Sunday, following the other days of the week.
14. D for Doc. The other letters are for Happy, Dopey, Bashful, Sleepy, Sneezy and Grumpy, the Seven Dwarves.

BACON & EGGS
Together Forever

Pair up these mixed groups with their natural partners.

FOOD

Roast Beef	Cheese
Macaroni	Mash
Strawberries	Pepper
Salt	Marmalade
Toast	Yorkshire Pudding
Sausage	Cream

FOLK

Superman	Jackie Onassis
John F. Kennedy	Cleopatra
Jennifer Aniston	Prince Albert
Queen Victoria	Ken
Barbie	Lois Lane
Antony	Brad Pitt

FICTION

Harry Potter	Gretel
Bilbo Baggins	Jane
Romeo	Hermione Granger
Sherlock Holmes	Juliet
Tarzan	Doctor Watson
Hansel	Gandalf

FUNNIES

Tom	Stimpy
Ren	Wilma
Beauty	Jerry
Fred	Lisa
Bart	Chicken
Cow	Beast

SOLUTIONS

FOOD: Roast Beef and Yorkshire Pudding. Macaroni and Cheese. Strawberries and Cream. Salt and Pepper. Toast and Marmalade. Sausage and Mash. FOLK: Superman and Lois Lane. John F. Kennedy and Jackie Onassis. Jennifer Aniston and Brad Pitt. Queen Victoria and Prince Albert. Barbie and Ken. Antony and Cleopatra. FICTION: Harry Potter and Hermione Granger. Bilbo Baggins and Gandalf. Romeo and Juliet. Sherlock Holmes and Doctor Watson. Hansel and Gretel. FUNNIES: Tom and Jerry. Ren and Stimpy. Beauty and Beast. Fred and Wilma. Bart and Lisa. Cow and Chicken.

SHORT CHANGE
A Tipping Yarn

Three men stay at a hotel for the night. The innkeeper charges £30 per room per night. The men rent one room; each pays £10. The hotel porter leads the men to their room. Later, the innkeeper discovers he has overcharged the men and asks the porter to return £5 to them. On the way upstairs, the porter realises that £5 can't be split evenly among three men, so he decides to keep £2 for himself and return £1 to each man. At this point, the three men have paid £9 each, totalling £27 and the porter has £2, which adds up to £29. Where did the 30th pound go?

SOLUTION

The mistake is in how the £30 is accounted for. The £2 that the porter has is part of the £27 the men have paid. A correct accounting of the money is that £27 was paid and £3 was not, totalling £30.

WORDOODLES

Say what you see

**Each of these Wordoodles is a word,
phrase or saying, cunningly disguised!
For example:
minI'LL BE THEREute
would mean: "I'll be there in a minute!"
See how you get on with these...**

1. arrest
   you're

2. somewhere
   rainbow

3. he art

4. pPPod

5. -> Class <-
   Class
   Class

6. STANDING
   miss

7. MEREPEAT

8. m ce
   m ce
   m ce

9. horobod

10. OturnedUT

SOLUTIONS

10. Turned inside out.
7. Repeat after me. 8. Three blind mice (No i's!). 9. Robin Hood.
4. Two peas in a pod. 5. Top class. 6. Misunderstanding.
1. You're under arrest. 2. Somewhere over the rainbow. 3. Broken heart.

62

STASH THE CASH

Hunt up the Volume

A friend told Trevor that someone has stashed a £50 note in a book in the local library. The friend doesn't know the title of the book but goes on to tell Trevor that the money is hidden between pages 201 and 202 of the unnamed book.

With this information, does Trevor ransack the library looking for the right book and the money, or does he laugh off the whole matter? Why?

SOLUTION

Trevor laughs off his friend's report. Every professionally made book numbers its pages by using odd numbers on right-hand pages and even numerals on left-hand pages. No one could have put anything between 201 (a right-hand page) and 202 (a left-hand page)!

FIGURE IT OUT

Mathematical Puzzles

1. I have four cats. I went and rounded up some mice for my cats to eat and put them in a cage. The first and biggest cat went into the cage and ate half of what she found and one more.
The second largest cat then went in and ate half of what he found and one more. The third cat then went in and ate half of what he found and one more. The fourth and smallest cat then ate half of what she found and one more and the mice were all gone. How many mice were there to begin with?

2. Two trains travel towards each other on the same track, beginning 100 miles apart. One train travels at 40 miles per hour; the other travels at 60 miles an hour. A bird starts flying in the same place as the fast train, flying at a speed of 90 miles per hour. When it reaches the slower train, it turns around, flying the other direction at the same speed. When it reaches the faster train again, it turns around - and so on. When the trains meet, how far will the bird have flown?

3. A fish is fifteen inches long. Its head is as long as its tail. If the head were twice as long as it really is,
the head and tail would together be as long as the middle bit of the fish.
How long is each part of the fish?

SOLUTIONS

3. The head and tail are each three inches long; the middle is nine.

2. Since the trains are 100 miles apart, and the trains are travelling toward each other at 40 and 60 mph, the trains will meet in one hour. The bird will have been flying for an hour at 90 miles per hour, so the bird will have travelled 90 miles.

1. 30.

DROODLES
Picture Puzzles

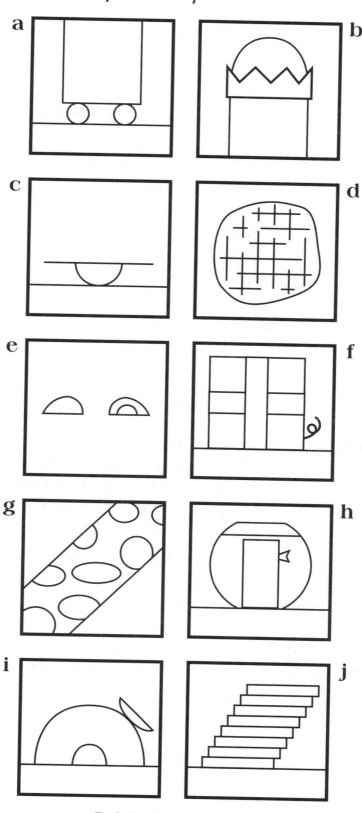

a

b

c

d

e

f

g

h

i

j

SOLUTIONS

a. Elephant on roller skates. b. Finger prince. c. Fried egg sunnyside down.
d. Waffle squished by Elephant. e. Cat winking. f. Gift pig.
g. Giraffe walking past window. h. Goldfish in telephone box.
i. Igloo with satellite dish. j. Leaning tower of pizza.

DOUBLE DUTCH
Codes & Ciphers

1

After school on Monday, Hermione found
this note in code taped to her desk:

Yg ctg jcxkpi c uwtrtkug rctva hqt
Ou. Dtqyp.

At first, she had no idea what it meant.
Then someone whispered in her ear,
"M stands for K." Just that clue helped
Hermione crack the code. Just as well, or
Hermione might have missed out!

2

Below is another "cryptogram" —
a sentence in which one set of letters is
substituted for another, but this time, it's
not so easy because the letters are more
randomly changed. The words are in their
right order, with a space after each. The
answer tells you what life was like before
the invention of the video recorder.

HJLNL ORTT VTOVXW QL HOY SYKRLW
XYM OVIH HY WLL YI HLTLKRWRYI,
QYHJ YI VH HJL WVSL HRSL.

SOLUTIONS

THE LION'S LEAP TONIGHT

A deadly decision

A Victorian explorer was once captured by a tribe whose chief decided that really, the man should die. However, the chief was a reasonable man and gave the explorer a choice: the explorer was to make a single statement. If it was true, he would be thrown off a high cliff. If it was false, he would be eaten by lions. What clever statement did the explorer make that forced the chief to let him go?

SOLUTION

The explorer made the statement, "I will be killed by lions." Now, if the chief feeds him to the lions, his statement will have been true, so he should have been thrown off the cliff. But if he is thrown off the cliff, his statement will have been false. The chief had to let the explorer go!

WHAT AM I?

Mystery Objects

1. Every creature in the world has seen me. But to their dying day they'll never see me again.

2. Weight in my belly,
   trees on my back,
   nails in my ribs,
   feet I do lack.
   What am I?

3. Bright as diamonds,
   loud as thunder,
   never still,
   a thing of wonder.
   What am I?

4. I build up castles.
   I tear down mountains.
   I make some men blind,
   I help others to see.
   What am I?

5. I fly without wings,
   drop without fear,
   but held in warm hands,
   I will soon disappear.
   What am I?

6. Until I am measured
   I am not known,
   yet how you miss me
   when I have flown.
   What am I?

SOLUTIONS

1. Yesterday. 2. A ship. 3. Fireworks. 4. Sand. 5. A snowflake. 6. Time.

SHORT & SWEET
Figures of Speech

Here are a bunch of well known phrases involving numbers. Each has been shortened to just numbers and initials. For example: "26 = L of the A" would be 26 Letters of the Alphabet. We'll supply a few clues, see how you get on with these ...

1. 64 = S on a C
   Clue: Pawn

2. 6 = P on a S T
   Clue: Cue

3. 7 = D with S W
   Clue: Fairy Story

4. 10 = E in a D
   Clue: Athletics

5. 4 = S in a Y
   Clue: Spring

6. 8 = L on a S
   Clue: Creepy Crawly

7. 9 = L of a C
   Clue: Miaow

8. 1 = H on a U
   Clue: Mythical Beast

9. 26 = M in a M
   Clue: Long race

10. 6 = S to a C

SOLUTIONS

1. 64 Squares on a Chessboard. 2. 6 Pockets on a Snooker Table. 3. 7 Dwarves with Snow White. 4. 10 Events in a Decathlon. 5. 4 Seasons in a Year. 6. 8 Legs on a Spider. 7. 9 Lives of a Cat. 8. 1 Horn on a Unicorn. 9. 26 Miles in a Marathon. 10. 6 Sides to a Cube.

ANNOYING
Short Riddles

These questions aren't as simple as they first appear!

1. How long did the Hundred Years' War last?

2. Which country makes Panama hats?

3. From which animal do we get "catgut"?

4. In which month do Russians celebrate the October Revolution?

5. What is a camel hair brush made of?

6. The Canary Islands in the Pacific are named after what animal?

7. What was King George VI's first name?

8. What colour is a purple finch?

9. What country do Chinese gooseberries come from?

10. How long did the Thirty Years' War last?

SOLUTIONS

10. Thirty years, of course. From 1618 to 1648.
8. Bright red. 9. New Zealand, it's another term for a kiwi fruit.
the name of her beloved husband.
Queen Victoria that no future king should ever be called Albert, as this was
7. Albert. When he came to the throne in 1936 he respected the wish of
6. The Latin name was Insularia Canaria - Island of the Dogs.
5. Squirrel fur.
4. November, the Russian calendar was 13 days behind ours.
3. From sheep and horses.
1. 116 years, from 1337 to 1453. 2. Ecuador.

THE KIPPING VICAR

A Tall story?

One day after dinner, my uncle sat me down and began to tell me a tale. There was once a minister who often fell asleep during Sunday services. One Sunday, he nodded off and dreamt that he was in the French Revolution! In this dream he was awaiting execution. His head was placed in the guillotine, and the blade was dropped. But just as it was about to hit, in real life, the minister's wife, noticing that he was asleep, jabbed him in the back of the neck with a knitting needle to wake him up. The minister was so startled by this, he jolted awake and immediately died of a heart attack! Hmm. Was my uncle telling me a true tale?

SOLUTION

No. If he died immediately, no-one would know what the minister was dreaming about!

1. What goes around the world yet stays in a corner?

2. What gets wetter the more it dries?

3. The more there is the less you see... What is it?

4. The capital of Turkey is a long word. Can you spell it?

5. Rearrange the letters of GROW NO LINSEED to spell one single word.

6. I have a head like a cat. I have feet like a cat. But I am not a cat. What am I?

7. What is in the middle of nowhere?

8. How much is a skunk worth?

9. What question can you never answer "yes" to?

10. How can FOUR be HALF of FIVE?

11. What Spanish instrument's name sounds like what a fisherman does?

12. What goes up and never comes down?

13. What's the difference between here and there?

14. What cheese is made backwards?

15. What can't you keep until you have given it to someone?

16. If Dick's father is Tom's son, what relation is Dick to Tom?

17. What do the dead eat, that the living would die if they ate it?

18. What can fill a room but takes up no space?

19. What is bought by the yard and worn by the foot?

20. How can you stand behind your friend as he stands behind you?

21. Who always goes to bed with his shoes on?

22. What goes through a door but never goes in and never comes out?

23. What is put on a table, cut, but never eaten?

24. What kind of coat can be put on only when wet?

25. What has six legs, two heads, four ears, two hands, but walks on four feet?

SOLUTIONS

1. A stamp. 2. A towel. 3. Darkness. 4. It. 5. ONE SINGLE WORD 6. A kitten. 7. The letter H. 8. A phew quid. 9. "Are you asleep?" (Or "Are you dead?") 10. The Roman Numeral FOUR (IV) appears in the middle of the English word Five: FIVE) 11. Castanet (cast a net!) 12. Your age. 13. The letter T. 14. Edam ('made' spelt backwards). 15. A promise. 16. Tom is Dick's grandfather. 17. Nothing. 18. Light. 19. Carpet. 20. By standing back to back. 21. A horse. 22. The keyhole. 23. A pack of cards. 24. A coat of paint! 25. A horse and rider.

WHERE IN THE WORLD?

Country Collection

Each of these pics represents the name of a country somewhere in the world... How many can you crack?

WHERE IN THE WORLD?

Country Collection

f

g

h

SOLUTIONS

MATCH OF THE DAY
Matchstick Puzzles

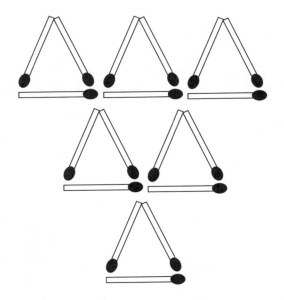

In the figure above, there are 6 small triangles,
and 1 larger triangle.
Reposition 6 matches to make
6 equal-sized diamonds.

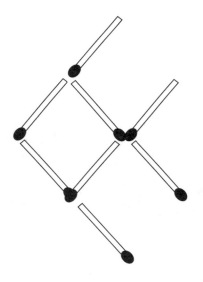

Reposition 3 matches to make the fish swim in
the opposite direction.

Answers on page 157

FIGURE IT OUT
Mathematical Puzzles

1. One boy can eat 100 chocolates in half a minute, and another can eat half as many in twice the length of time. How many chocolates can both boys eat in 15 seconds?

2. Farmer Joe came to town with some watermelons. He sold half of them plus half a melon, and found that he had one whole melon left. How many melons did he take to town?

3. Sally promised Kate today that she will tell Kate a big secret on the day before four days from the day after tomorrow. If today is Saturday the 13th, on what day and date will Sally tell Kate her big secret?

4. When asked how old she was, Mary replied, "In two years I will be twice as old as I was five years ago." How old is she?

5. Lily has an unusual habit that slows her down - she takes one step backward for every two she takes forward. How many steps will it take her to get from the couch to the fridge, which is twenty paces?

WRITE STUFF
Word Puzzles & Teasers

1. Using the same letters in the same order, can you fill in the blanks and make a normal sentence of this?

A   _o_a_l_   doctor had   _o   _a_l_ and therefore, was   _o_t_   a_b_l_e_ to operate.

2. Which of the following words don't belong in the group and why?

CORSET, COSTER, SECTOR, ESCORT, COURTS.

3. What five letters can be made into four different words that fill in these blanks?

The farmer with hundreds of _ _ _ _ _ , (sheep) deeply _ _ _ _ _ about the amount of rainfall, and _ _ _ _ _ around with artificial watering systems when the ground is dry enough to _ _ _ _ _ him about the possibility of crop failure.

4. What's so special about this sentence?

A big cuddly dog emitted fierce growls, happily ignoring joyful kids licking minute nuts on pretty queer rotten smelly toadstools underneath vampires who x-rayed young zombies.

SOLUTIONS

4. The first letter of each word makes up the entire alphabet in order!
3. Acres, Cares, Races, Scare.
2. Courts. All of the others are anagrams of each other.
1. 'N O T A B L E'
A NOTABLE doctor had NO TABLE and therefore, was NOT ABLE to operate.

SPY PHONE
The Numbers of Nations

Otto Von Hapsblunk, the international spy, always has the latest spy equipment. Can you work out which pieces of essential spy kit he can order by dialling the following numbers on his spy phone?

a. 3632987752 1948 b. 25849583

c. 199761952 758976

d. 8974618838 e. 85363977 5308

f. 2723 1775 g. 48176574 4775

h. 307672574 737

i. 832839 216381 j. 3153 71887789

SOLUTIONS

a. Electronic bugs. b. Disguise. c. Automatic Pistol. d. Sunglasses. e. Skeleton keys. f. Code Book. g. Grappling Hook. h. Exploding Pen. i. Secret Camera. j. Fake Passport.

TANGRAM
Chinese Puzzle

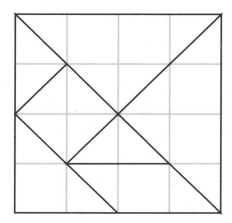

The Tangram is an ancient puzzle, and an art, brought to Europe from China many centuries ago. The seven pieces of the the Tangram above can be arranged to make hundreds of different designs. Make your own tangram from the pattern above, and see if you can create the shapes below. You must use all seven pieces for each design. Then make up your own designs and challenge a friend!

a. The triangle

b. The two squares

c. The Rooster

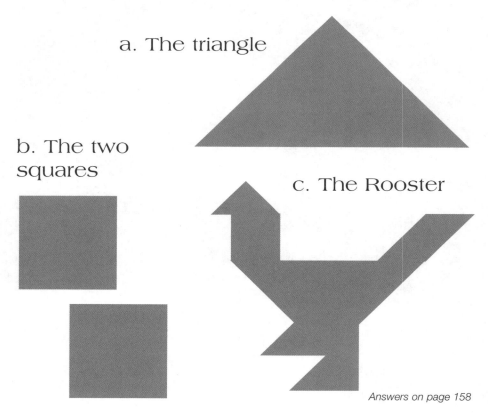

Answers on page 158

WORDOODLES

Say what you see

Each of these Wordoodles is a word, phrase or saying, cunningly disguised! For example:
minI'LL BE THEREute
would mean: "I'll be there in a minute!"
See how you get on with these...

1. Bend
   Backwards

2. sleeping
       job

3. winter
      coat

4. VAD   ERS

5. blueoncemoon

6. Head
   LOheelsVE

7. STEP PETS PETS

8. bridge
   water

9. I right I

10. Mill 1 ion

SOLUTIONS

1. Bend over backwards. 2. Sleeping on the job. 3. Winter overcoat.
4. Space invaders. 5. Once in a blue moon. 6. Head over heels in love.
7. One step forwards, two steps back. 8. Water under the bridge.
9. Right between the eyes. 10. One in a million.

DUMB & DUMBER

How stupid do you feel?

This is a selection of tricky riddles that might make you feel stupid when you hear the answers!

1. In what month of the year do American people always eat least?

2. Can you name three consecutive days without using the letter "u"?

3. Scientists have proven that cats have more hair on one side than their other side. Some people believe that this is because when cats lie on their side they need insulation from the cold on the floor or ground. Which side of a cat has more hair?

4. If a car drives due north for 2.5 miles and at the end of the trip is facing due south, how is that possible?

5. There once were three houses. A blue house, a red house, and a white house. The red house was not on the left and the blue house was not in the middle or on the right. Where is the White House?

6. There is an ancient invention still used in some parts of the world today that allows people to see through walls. What is it?

SOLUTIONS

LUCKY DIP

General Riddles

1. If the day before the day after tomorrow will be Saturday, and the day after the day before yesterday was Thursday, what is today?

2. The amount of water flowing into a tank doubles every minute. The tank is full in an hour. When was the tank half full?

3. I am a path situated between two mountains. Take away my first letter and you leave a path situated between two buildings. What am I?

4. Lucy had it first, Ethel had it last, Mary Lungel had it twice until she married Peter Stupid and never had it again. What is it?

5. As I went across the bridge, I met a man with a load of wood which was neither straight nor crooked. What kind of wood was it?

6. The Pope has it but he does not use it. Your father has it but your mother probably uses it too. Nuns do not have it, neither does Madonna. What is it?

SOLUTIONS

1. Friday. 2. At 59 minutes. 3. A Valley. Take away the V and I'm an Alley. 4. The letter L. 5. Sawdust. 6. A last name.

PIC & MIX
Silly Word Puzzles

1. What do you get if you cross a cow and a jogging machine?

2. What do you get if you cross a biscuit with an elephant?

3. What do you get if you cross a satchel with a mallard?

4. What do you get if you cross an elephant and a bottle of whisky?

5. What do you get if you cross a skeleton and a dog?

6. What do you get if you cross teeth with candy?

7. What do you get if you cross a toadstool and a full suitcase?

8. What do you get if you cross an owl with a skunk?

9. What do you get if you cross a penguin and an elk?

10. What do you get if you cross a bottle of washing up liquid and a mouse?

11. What do you get when you cross a giraffe and a rooster?

12. What do you get if you cross a flock of sheep and a radiator?

13. What do you get if you cross a dog with a game of football?

14. What do you get when you cross a cheetah and a pizza?

15. What do you get if you cross a student and an alien?

16. What do you get if you cross a pudding and a skunk?

17. What do you get if you cross an alligator and King Midas?

18. What do you get if you cross a singer and a tall ladder?

19. What do you get if you cross a monster and a chicken?

20. What do you get if you cross a frog with a traffic warden?

21. What do you get if you cross a snake with a building site?

22. What do you get when you cross an octopus and a cow?

23. What do you get if you cross a pig and a box of itching powder?

24. What do you get when you cross a old lady and an octopus?

25. What do you get if you cross a bear with a freezer?

SOLUTIONS

1. A milk shake! 2. Crumbs! 3. A ducksack! 4. Trunk and disorderly! 5. An animal that buries itself in the garden! 6. Dental floss! 7. Not mushroom for your clothes! 8. A bird that smells but doesn't give a hoot! 9. A chocolate moose! 10. Bubble and squeak! 11. An animal that wakes up people on the top floor! 12. Central bleating! 13. Spot the ball! 14. Fast food! 15. Something from another university! 16. A smelly jelly! 17. A croc of gold! 18. Someone who can easily get the high notes! 19. Free strange eggs! 20. Toad away! 21. A boa-constructor! 22. An animal that can milk itself! 23. Pork scratchings! 24. I don't know, but it's really good at Bingo! 25. A teddy brrrr!

FIGURE IT OUT
Mathematical Puzzles

1. Frankie decides to drive to an isolated spa for the weekend. He drives 3 miles east, then makes a sharp left and drives 4 miles north. How many miles could he have saved if he could have driven there in a straight line?

2. Alice, Ben, Charlie, David, and Ed entered a contest to guess how many jelly beans are in a jar. Alice guessed 30, Ben guessed 28, Charlie guessed 29, David guessed 25, and Ed guessed 26. Two were off the mark by 1, one was wrong by 4, and one by 3. But one was correct. How many jelly beans are in the jar at the store?

3. A girl is twice as old as her brother and half as old as her father. In 22 years, her brother will be half as old as his father. How old is the daughter now?

4. Jack and Jill took turns driving on a round trip using the same route both ways. Jack drove the first 40 miles and then Jill drove the rest of the way. Jack started to drive on the return trip and then Jill drove the last 50 miles. Which of the two drove more miles and how many more did the person drive?

SOLUTIONS

1. The answer is 2 miles. If you join the start point of Frankie's journey to the end, the whole journey makes a triangle with a right-angle (an angle of exactly 90 degrees). In any right-angled triangle, the square of the hypotenuse, or longest side, is equal to the squares of the other two sides added together. 3 x 3 is 9, 4 x 4 is 16. added together these sides' squares make 25. So the longest side must be 5 miles long (because 5 x 5 = 25) and Frankie has driven 7 miles. 7 - 5 = 2

2. There are 29 jelly beans in the jar. 3. 22 years old.

4. Jill drove 20 miles more than Jack. Example, if it was a 300 mile round trip, Jack must have driven 140 miles, and Jill drove 160 miles. You can set the distance of the trip at any length, and the difference will always be 20 miles.

YOUR NAME IS MUD!

Whose footprints?

One of the triplets left muddy footprints all over the kitchen floor. Since all three wear the same size shoes, their mum and dad can't tell which triplet should clean up the floor.

"I didn't do it," said Annie.

"Danny did it," said Fanny.

"Fanny is lying," said Danny.

Only one of the triplets is telling the truth - the other two are lying.

Whose footprints are on the kitchen floor?

SOLUTION

Annie left the footprints. Remember, only one triplet can be telling the truth. If Danny did it, then both Fanny and Annie are telling the truth. If Fanny did it, then Danny is telling the truth when he says that Fanny is lying. With Annie as the culprit, Annie is lying by claiming she is innocent, Fanny is lying by accusing Danny, and Danny is the one who is telling the truth.

PANTS ON FIRE!

Who's telling the truth?

1. Four friends left one slice of pizza in the kitchen and went into the next room to play games. During the next half hour, each friend left the room for a few minutes and then returned. At the end of the hour, all four went back into the kitchen and found that the last slice of pizza was gone.
Use the following statements to figure out who ate it. Only ONE of the following statements is true.

Linda: "Mike ate it."

Mike: "Olive ate it."

Ned: "Who me? Can't be."

Olive: "Mike is lying when he says I ate it."

2. Cindy, Andy, and Mia, were all over at Keith's house when a package was delivered. Each child guessed what was in the box, but only one of them was right. Using their guesses as clues, can you figure out what was in the box?

Cindy said, "It's a laptop computer."

Andy said, "I'll bet it's a pizza."

Mia said, "I think a picture or a laptop computer is in the box."

"It's a picture, for sure," said Keith.

SOLUTIONS

1. Ned ate the last slice of pizza. It's impossible for Linda's, Mike's, or Ned's statement to be the only one that is true. (If Linda's statement that Mike ate it is true, then Ned's statement is also true. If Mike's statement that Olive ate it is true, then Ned's statement is also true.) If Ned's statement is true, then no one else's statement can be true. Therefore, Ned's statement is false.

2. A pizza was in the box. Right away, you can tell that Mia can't be right, because if she is, then Keith would also be right (they both said picture), and no more than one child can be right. And since Mia is wrong, then Cindy is wrong, too, because they both said laptop computer. That means that Andy is correct - it's a pizza.

88

WHAT AM I?

Mystery Objects

1. How are a jeweller and a jailer alike?
2. I know a word of letters three,
Add two more and fewer there will be.
3. What can't be burned in fire,
nor drowned in water?
4. What do you fill with empty hands?
5. What do you serve that you can't eat?
6. What gets whiter the dirtier that it gets?
7. What grows when it eats,
but dies when it drinks?
8. What is in the middle of nowhere?
9. What runs but doesn't walk?
10. What 3 letters change a girl
into a woman?
11. What turns everything around but
does not move?
12. Which moves faster: heat or cold?
13. Hard or soft, I move with equal speed.
What am I?
14. You can walk on the pointy tips of my
blades and feel no pain. What am I?
15. I get short when I get old.
I go out then I get cold. What am I?
16. I can be sharp as a blade
or dull as a grey sky:
you'd be mad to lose me. What am I?
17. What can you catch but not throw?
18. No sooner spoken than broken.
19. I am only useful when I am full,
yet I am always full of holes. What am I?
20. "Look in my face, I am somebody.
Look at my back, I am nobody."

SOLUTIONS

1. The jeweller sells watches and the jailer watches cells.
2. Few. 3. Ice. 4. Gloves. 5. A tennis ball. 6. A blackboard.
7. Fire. 8. The letter H. 9. Water. 10. AGE. 11. A mirror.
12. Heat. (Everybody can catch a cold.) 13. Water. 14. Grass. 15. A candle.
16. Your mind. 17. A cold. 18. Silence. 19. A sieve. 20. A mirror.

89

APPLIANCE OF SCIENCE
Scientific Puzzles

1. There are two plastic jugs filled with water. How could you put all of this water into a barrel, without using the jugs or any dividers, and still tell which water came from which jug?

2. You have a ping pong ball at the bottom of a curvy, skinny hole in the ground 20 foot deep. You want to get it out but you can't stick your hand in — it won't reach or fit.
A string won't work because you won't be able to attatch it.
What can you do to get it out without digging a hole?

3. A large truck is crossing a bridge 10 miles long. The bridge can hold only 14,000 lbs, which is the exact weight of the truck. The truck makes it half way across the bridge and stops.
A bird lands on the truck.
Does the bridge collapse? Give a reason.

4. Two identical tanks full of water are being drained at the same time. One of the tanks has one two-centimetre circular drain outlet and the other has two one-centimetre circular drain outlets.
Will one of the tanks empty faster than the other?

SOLUTIONS

1. Freeze them first. Take them out of the jugs and put the ice in the barrel. You will be able to tell which water came from which jug.
2. Put water in the hole. The pingpong ball will float to the top.
3. No, it does not collapse, because it has driven 5 miles - you can subtract the petrol used from the total weight of the truck.
4. The tank with the one 2-centimetre drain outlet has twice the area as two 1-centimetre outlets and will therefore empty first.

JUST FOR THE RECORD
The tale of the tape

A man was found shot dead in his study. He was slumped over his desk and a gun was in his hand. There was a cassette recorder on his desk. When the police entered the room and pressed the play button on the tape recorder they heard, "I can't go on. I have nothing to live for." Then there was the sound of a gunshot. How did the detective immediately know that the man had been murdered?

SOLUTION

The cassette had started at the beginning of the man's statement, who would have rewound it?

WHO DUNNIT

Crime Puzzles

1. Late one evening Claire Vermont looked through the bay windows of her living room and to her horror saw a man strangling a woman. Claire's first impulse was to open the door and attempt to stop the attack. However, she did not. She also did not immediately phone the police, although the telephone was in perfect working order. She was unable to stop the crime in spite of the fact that she was not physically constrained in any way. She did not even call out for assistance to her butler, although he was in the house. Can you explain her strange behaviour?

2. This is a true story from Taiwan. A rich man's son was kidnapped. The ransom note told him to bring a valuable diamond to a phone booth in the middle of a public park. Plainclothes police officers surrounded the park, intending to follow the criminal or his messenger. The rich man arrived at the phone booth and followed instructions but the police were powerless to prevent the diamond from leaving the park and reaching the crafty villain.
What did he do?
A clue:
The phone box wasn't empty.

SOLUTIONS

1. Claire Vermont saw the murder from outside her home looking in. She had no keys to the house, and the man committing the murder was her butler.
2. When the rich man reached the phone booth he found a carrier pigeon in a cage. It had a message attached telling the man to put the diamond in a small bag which was around the pigeon's neck and to release the bird. When the man did this the police were powerless to follow the bird as it returned across the city to its owner.

LUCKY DIP
General Riddles

1. Two men play five games of chess. Each man wins the same number of games. There are no draws. Explain this.

2. If today is Tuesday, what is the day after the day before the day before tomorrow?

3. There is one word in the English language that is always pronounced incorrectly. What is it?

4. What relationship to you is your father's only brother's wife's only brother-in-law?

5. How much food can you eat on an empty stomach?

6. Where will you find roads without cars, forests without trees and cities without any houses?

7. What is black when you buy it, red when you use it, and grey when you throw it away?

8. What regularly changes shape, yet remains a sphere, is always there, but often not seen?

SOLUTIONS

1. The two men weren't playing each other. 2. Tuesday. 3. The word "incorrectly". 4. It's your father. 5. Only one bite. After that the stomach isn't empty any more. 6. On a map. 7. Coal. 8. The Moon.

General Riddles

1. When can you add two to eleven and get one?

2. If you turn your right-handed glove inside out and put it on your left hand, where will the palm of the glove be on your left hand?

3. Here on Earth it's almost always true, that tomorrow will follow today. Yet there is a place where yesterday always follows today. Where is this place?

4. What book was once owned by only the wealthy, but now everyone can have it? You can't buy it in a book shop or take it out from a library?

5. If you cross out all unnecessary letters in the following string of letters, a logical sentence will remain. Can you see it?
**AALLLOUGNINCEACELSS
SEANRYTELNETCTEERS**

6. A man was outside taking a walk when it began to rain. He did not have an umbrella and he wasn't wearing a hat. His clothes were soaked, yet not a single hair on his head got wet.
How could this happen?

SOLUTIONS

6. The man was bald!
remaining letters will spell "A LOGICAL SENTENCE".
5. If you cross out the letters in "ALL UNNECESSARY LETTERS", then the
3. In a dictionary.   4. A Telephone Book.
2. The palm of the glove will be against your left hand palm.
1. When you add two hours to eleven o'clock, you get one o'clock.

RESCUE STATIONS
One jump or two?

A fireman is running to get a net under a lady who looks like she might jump from the window of her 20-storey apartment building. There is nothing below her except a 20-storey fall. The fireman is still 100 yards away when she falls and he can't get there in time. The woman is not hurt. How is that possible?

SOLUTION
She fell inwards.

FIGURE IT OUT

Mathematical Puzzles

1. A bottle and a cork together cost £1.50 and the bottle costs £1.00 more than the cork. How much does each cost?

2. The ages of a father and a son add up to 55. The father's age is the son's age reversed. How old are they?

3. Robert and David between them can finish a job in 24 days. If Robert works at two-thirds David's speed, how long would it take each of them to finish the job on their own?

4. Divide 30 by half and add 10. What do you get?

5. How many 3-cent stamps in a dozen? 3, 4, 12 or 6?

6. The ages of a father and son add up to 66. The father's age is the son's age reversed.
How old could they be? (There are three possible solutions).

7. I am the owner of a pet shop. If I put in one canary per cage, I have one bird too many. If I put in two canaries per cage, I have one cage too many. How many cages and canaries do I have?

SOLUTIONS

1. The bottle costs £1.25 and the cork costs £0.25.
2. Father is 41, the son is 14. 3. Robert = 60 Days, David = 40 Days.
4. 70. 30 divided by a half is 60, + 10 is 70. 5. Twelve.
6. 51 and 15, 42 and 24, 60 and 06. 7. I have 3 cages and 4 canaries.

STUPID ANSWERS

To sensible questions

1. Why do traffic lights turn red?

2. Why did the Romans build straight roads?

3. Why are elephants wrinkly?

4. Why do traffic wardens have yellow stripes on their hats?

5. Why do elephants have grey skin?

6. Why do cyclists wear lycra shorts?

7. Why do birds fly south for the winter?

8. Why can't your nose be 12 inches long?

9. Why is Alabama the cleverest state in the USA?

10. Why did the gum cross the road?

11. Why do surgeons wear masks?

12. Why is Britain so wet?

SOLUTIONS

1. You would too if you had to change in the middle of the street! 2. So their soldiers didn't go around the bend! 3. Because they hate being ironed! 4. To stop people parking on their faces! 5. To keep their insides from falling out! 6. Because if they didn't, they'd be arrested! 7. It's quicker than walking! 8. Because then it would be a foot! 9. Because it has 4 A's and one B! 10. Because it was stuck to the chicken's foot! 11. So if somebody makes a mistake nobody will know who did it! 12. Because the Queen has reigned there for 50 years!

WORDOODLES

Say what you see

Each of these Wordoodles is a word, phrase or saying, cunningly disguised! For example: minI'LL BE THEREute would mean: "I'll be there in a minute!" See how you get on with these...

1. ENDSSDNE

2. e
   a
   v
   e
   s

3. Stand
   I

4. OHOLENE

5. T M
   A U
   H S
   W T

6. R | E | A | D | I | I | N | G

7. MAN
   BOARD

8. Eye E
   See Except

9. YOUJUSTME

10. DDDWESTDDD

SOLUTIONS

1. Making ends meet. 2. Eavesdrop. 3. I understand. 4. Hole in one. 5. What goes up, must come down. 6. Reading between the lines. 7. Man overboard. 8. i before e except after c. 9. Just between you and me. 10. West Indies.

DROODLES
Picture Puzzles

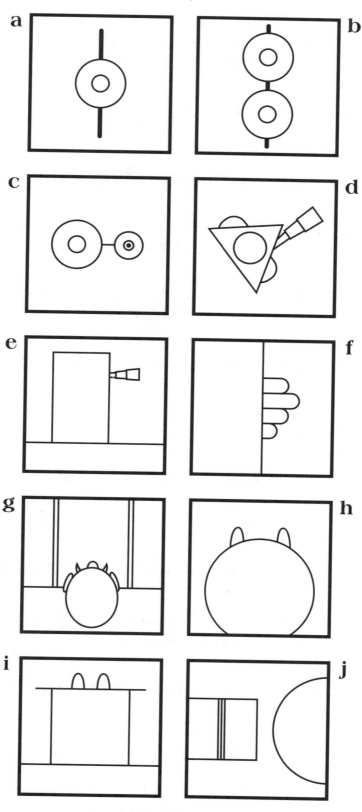

SOLUTIONS

a. Mexican on a bicycle. b. 2 Mexicans on a tandem. c. Mexican frying an egg. d. Nelson looking through a telescope. e. Nelson in a phone box. f. Napoleon's coat. g. Olympic swimming elephant. h. Rabbit blowing bubblegum. i. Rabbit in hat. j. Ronnie O'Sullivan.

STUPID ANSWERS

To sensible questions

1. Why can't you bury people who live opposite a graveyard?

2. Why shouldn't you put a cat in the washing machine?

3. Why do babies walk softly?

4. Why should you keep a pencil in the bedroom?

5. Why is there very little honey in Belgium?

6. Why do bagpipers walk when they play?

7. Why can't a bicycle stand on its own?

8. Why do monkeys scratch themselves?

9. Why was night cricket invented?

10. Why do elephants never forget?

11. Why aren't elephants allowed on beaches?

12. Why do chickens lay eggs?

SOLUTIONS

1. Because they're not dead! 2. In case you get a sock in the puss! 3. Because they can't walk hardly! 4. In case you want to draw the curtains! 5. Because there's only one B in Belgium! 6. To get away from the awful noise! 7. Because it's two-tyred! 8. Because they're the only ones who know where the itch is! 9. Because bats like to sleep in the daytime! 10. Because nobody ever tells them anything! 11. They can't keep their trunks up! 12. If they dropped them, they'd break!

LUCKY DIP
General Riddles

1. My daughter has as many sisters as she has brothers.
Each of her brothers has twice as many sisters as brothers. How many sons and daughters do I have?

2. Mr & Mrs Van Uden have five children.
Of these five, half are boys.
How is this possible?

3. Jason is lying dead, he has an iron bar across his back and some cheese in front of him.
What is Jason, and why did he die?

4. How can you make the following equation true by drawing only one straight line?
5+5+5=550

5. What has 3 heads, is ugly, and smells bad?

6. How can you throw a ball as hard as you can and have it come back to you, even if it doesn't hit anything, there is nothing attached to it, and no one else catches or throws it?

SOLUTIONS

1. Four daughters, three sons.
2. They are all boys, so half of them must be boys!
3. Jason is a mouse, in a mouse trap.
4. Draw a diagonal line on the first plus sign that turns it into a 4!
The equation then becomes true: 545+5=550
5. Oops, my mistake, you don't have 3 heads.
6. Throw the ball straight up in the air!

MISSION IMPOSSIBLE

Solving the unsolvable

1. You are on an island in the middle of a lake. The lake is in a remote part of the country and there has never been a bridge connecting the island to the mainland. Every day a tractor and wagon gives hayrides around the island. Puzzled as to how the tractor had gotten onto the island, you ask around and find out that the tractor was not transported to the island by boat or by air.
Nor was it built on the island.
How did the tractor got there?

2. On a fine sunny day a ship was in the harbour. All of a sudden the ship began to sink. There was no storm, nothing was placed on the ship, there were no holes in it and absolutely nothing was mechanically wrong with the ship.
Why did it sink?

3. Four cars come to a crossroads, each coming from a different direction.
They can't decide who got there first, so they all go at the same time. They do not crash into each other, but all four cars go.
How is this possible?

4. In 1990, a person is 15 years old.
In 1995 that same person is 10 years old.
How is this possible?

SOLUTIONS

1. It was driven over in winter when the lake was frozen.
2. It was a submarine. 3. They all turn left.
4. The years are "B.C.".... not A.D.

102

MATCH OF THE DAY
Matchstick Puzzles

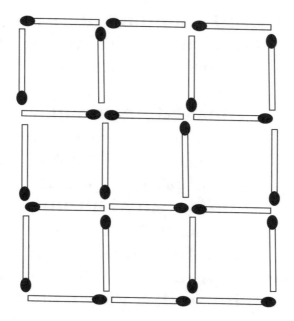

a) Take away 4 matches to leave 5 equal-sized squares
b) Take away 6 matches to leave 5 equal-sized squares
c) Take away 8 matches to leave 4 equal-sized squares

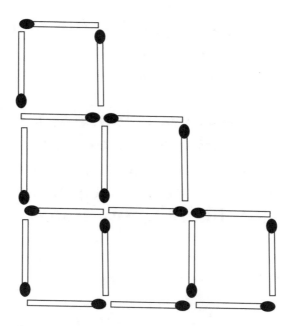

Take away 6 matches to leave 3 equal-sized squares.

Answers on page 157 / 158

WRITE STUFF
Word Puzzles & Teasers

Which word sounding the same, but spelled differently, could mean both of the following?

1. naked, mammal.
2. flower, lines.
3. snout, recognises.
4. rule, downpour.
5. sunbeams, lift up.
6. a dog's foot, skint.
7. painful, cutting tool.
8. sea creatures, British country.
9. chucked, a king's seat.
10. step, look at intensely.
11. castle, battled.
12. fog, avoided.
13. number, swallowed.
14. heaviness, delay.
15. captured, tennis pitch.

Which word spelled the same, but sounding different, could mean both of these?

16. argue, paddle a boat.
17. lean over, pretty knot.
18. bird of peace, jumped.
19. rip, something you cry.
20. figure, more numb.

SOLUTIONS

19. TEAR. 20. NUMBER.
15. CAUGHT, COURT. 16. ROW. 17. BOW. 18. DOVE.
12. MIST, MISSED. 13. EIGHT, ATE. 14. WEIGHT, WAIT.
9. THROWN, THRONE. 10. STAIR, STARE. 11. FORT, FOUGHT.
5. RAYS, RAISE. 6. PAW, POOR. 7. SORE, SAW. 8. WHALES, WALES.
1. BARE, BEAR. 2. ROSE, ROWS. 3. NOSE, KNOWS. 4. REIGN, RAIN.

PANTS PUZZLE

How many boxers?

Every Tuesday evening Mrs Mann drives up to her son Ben's cottage to visit. On these weekly visits she drops off his clean clothes and picks up his dirty laundry. Since Ben always wears his boxer shorts and changes his underwear every morning, what is the minimum number of pairs of boxers he can own?

SOLUTION

Fifteen. Every Tuesday Ben receives seven pairs of boxers and also leaves seven for his Mum to wash. That equals fourteen, plus the pair he is wearing.

WRITE STUFF
Word Puzzles & Teasers

1. These words all belong to the same logical family because they have something in common. What is it?
Footloose, committed, successful, address, millennium.
Which of the following words belong to the same family as the one above?
Silly, ancestor, millstone, heedless.

2. There is an animal hiding in each sentence below.
Can you find the animals?
For example, there's a bee in:
"I'll be eleven next month."

2a. We can go at five thirty.
2b. It's nice to do good deeds.
2c. Take soap and a flannel.
2d. Most rich cakes have chocolate on them.
2e. You can keep the watch or sell it.
2f. Use a ladder to clean the windows.
2g. It will be a rainy day.
2h. He came late to the dance.
2i. Tell me if I should leave now.
2j. Will a map help you?
2k. Don't cough at me, Tommo, use a hanky!
2l. That's not a Yeti, Gerbils are bigger!

3. What is it that when you take away the whole, you still have some left over?

4. What word, expression, or name is depicted here? GR12"AVE

5. By changing the second letter of each word below, you can make another valid word. Can you change each word such that the second letters will reveal an eleven-letter word when read downwards? Therefore, what now reads AWPYRNUCEPA will be a real word.

BAKE

SWAP

OPAL

DYED

ARKS

SNOW

LUMP

ACES

MELT

SPUN

RANT

6. You can take one letter out of the 9-letter word STARTLING so that without rearranging letters you will have a real 8-letter word: STARLING, which is a bird. Continue to remove one letter at a time to make new English words until you get down to a one-letter English word. Remember: do not rearrange any of the letters; just remove the letters one at a time to create 7 more real words.

7. The following anagram hides something that kids like to do. Adults can do it but, generally, not very well.
'ROAST MULES'

SOLUTIONS

FIGURE IT OUT

Mathematical Puzzles

1. If seven people meet each other and each shakes hands only once with each of the others, how many handshakes will there have been?

2. When asked how old she was, Suzie replied, "In two years I will be twice as old as I was five years ago." How old is she?

3. If five thousand, five hundred and five pounds is written as £5,505, how should twelve thousand, twelve hundred and twelve pounds be written?

4. Bill rode his bicycle 300 miles. Three tyres were used equally in accumulating this distance. How many miles of wear did each tyre sustain?

5. A car's milometer shows 72927 miles, a number which reads the same backwards. What are the minimum miles you would need to travel to get another number that does the same?

6. A new medical building containing 100 offices had just been completed. Dave was hired to paint the numbers 1 to 100 on the doors. How many times will Dave have to paint the number nine?

SOLUTIONS

90, 91, 92, 93, 94, 95, 96, 97, 98, 99.
6. Twenty times - 9, 19, 29, 39, 49, 59, 69, 79, 89,
5. 110 miles (73037).
total of 600 miles of wear. And 600 divided by three is 200.
mile of usage. Therefore, in a total of 300 miles traveled, there would be a
4. 200 miles. For every mile travelled, each of the two tyres sustained one
not do it again. 2. She's 12. 3. £13,212.
when A shakes hands with B, B has already shaken hands with A and need
1. Twenty-one. Most people would think there were 42 handshakes, but

NO PLACE LIKE ROME
The Soldier's dream

One morning a Roman soldier who had been on sentry duty the night before asked to see his centurion. "Last night I dreamed that hordes of Barbarians would sweep down from the north and attack our fort tonight!" he reported.
The centurion wasn't sure he believed in dreams coming true,
but he doubled the patrols, just in case.
That night, the Barbarians did indeed make their attack, but thanks to the extra patrols they were easily repelled. After the battle, the centurion thanked the soldier for his warning and then confined him to barracks for a month as a punishment. Why?

SOLUTION

The soldier had a dream, so he must have been asleep while he should have been on sentry duty the night before!

109

FIGURE IT OUT
Mathematical Puzzles

1. Jack and Jill are playing cards for a stake of £1 a game. At the end of the evening, Jack has won 3 games and Jill has won £3.
How many games did they play?

2. Each son in the Hubbard family has just as many brothers as sisters, but each daughter has twice as many brothers as sisters. How many boys and girls are there in the family?

3. It takes a clock two seconds to strike 2 o'clock. How long will it take to strike 3 o'clock?

4. There are 10 chocolate-making machines. Each of them makes chocolate balls of 10 grams each. Then one day, one of the machines breaks down, after which it makes chocolate balls of only 9.5 grams each. You are given only three chances to weigh the chocolates to find out which is the broken machine.
You can take any amount of chocolates you like from each machine. How are you going to find out which is the broken one?

5. Sabrina gave Samantha as many dollars as Samantha started out with. Samantha then gave Sabrina back as much as Sabrina had left. Sabrina then gave Samantha back as many dollars as Samantha had left, which left Sabrina broke and gave Samantha a total of $80.
How much did Sabrina and Samantha have at the beginning of their exchange?

6. A soft-hearted antique dealer often paid more than she should and sold for less than she could. As she was figuring out her costs and profits one day her sister said, "You sold that dish for only a 5 per cent profit. If you had bought it for 10 per cent less than you did pay, and sold it at the same price you did charge for it, you would have made a £15 profit." How much did the antique dealer pay for the dish?

7. It takes 10 snails 50 minutes to cross a path from when the first snail slithers onto the path to when the last snail leaves. The snails cross in single file and the path is wide enough to accommodate only 8 snails at a time. The snails travel at the same speed and each snail is on the path for the same length of time. How long is each snail on the path for?

8. Is half of two plus two equal to two or three?

SOLUTIONS

1. They played 9 games: Jack won 3 games, and Jill won 6 games.
2. There are 4 boys and 3 girls in the family: each boy has 3 brothers and 3 sisters, but each girl has 4 brothers and 2 sisters.
3. It will take 4 seconds. Since the clock strikes 2 o'clock in two seconds, these two seconds are the interval between two strikes. Between the first and the third strike there are two intervals, so it will be 4 seconds.
4. You only need to use the scales once. Take one ball from the first, two from the second, three from the third, four from the fourth, etc. There should be 55 balls of chocolate in total. Normally the chocolate balls would weigh 550 grams total. By looking at the amount of missing weight you can tell which machine is broken. For example, if only 0.5 grams is missing then machine one is broken, if 1 gram is missing then machine two is broken, if 1.5 grams is missing then machine three is broken, and so on.
5. Sabrina had $50 and Samantha had $30.
6. She paid £100 for the dish.
7. Twenty-five minutes. If the path is wide enough to accommodate 8 of the 10 snails then the first snail will be just leaving the path as the tenth snail is starting onto the path. Using that information you can simply divide the full 50 minutes by 2.
8. Three. It seems that it could almost be either, but if you follow the mathematical orders of operation, division is performed before addition. So… half of two is one. Then add two, and the answer is three.

THINK ABOUT IT!

Puzzles that aren't what they seem

At first glance these puzzles seem difficult, but they're not.
In each case there is a simple solution.

1. If I dropped a bowling ball in a bucket of water which is at 45 degrees Fahrenheit, and dropped another ball of the same weight, mass, and size in a bucket of water which is at 30 degrees Fahrenheit, dropping them at the same time, which ball would hit the bottom of the bucket first?

2. A man went outside without an umbrella or a raincoat, yet did not get wet. How's that?

3. Ten pears hanging high, ten men come passing by; each took a pear and left nine hanging there. How could that be?

4. A man drove to the local shop. He got out, and accidentally locked his keys in the car with the windows all shut. He went in the shop, and bought some milk. He came back out and was able to unlock the door without touching anything on the outside of the car. How did he do it?

SOLUTIONS

4. The car was a convertible and he reached inside to open the door.
3. "Each" is the name of one of the men, and he's the only one that took a pear.
2. It wasn't raining.
1. The ball in the bucket of 45 degree Fahrenheit water would hit the bottom of the bucket first. The 30 degree F water is frozen!

112

EYES ON THE PRIZE
To swap... or not?

You are on a game show.
You are shown three closed doors.
A prize is hidden behind one, and the
game show host knows where it is.
You are asked to select a door.
You do. Before you open it, the host
opens one of the other doors, showing
that it is empty, then asks you if you'd
like to change your guess. Should you,
should you not, or doesn't it matter?

SOLUTION

Remember that the host knows where the prize is.
When you pick a door, there's a 66.7% chance you're wrong.
If you're wrong, the host will always open the one door left that doesn't
contain the prize. So if you were wrong (66.7% chance), you're better off
switching to the door that the host leaves closed.

LUCKY DIP
General Riddles

1. If your friend says to you, "I'll bet you £1 that if you give me £2, I will give you £3 in return", would this be a good bet for you to accept?

2. If you go to the movies and you're paying, is it cheaper to take one friend to the movies twice, or two friends to the movies at the same time?

3. If two hours ago, it was exactly as long after one o'clock in the afternoon as it was before one o'clock in the morning, what time would it be now?

4. When the day after tomorrow is yesterday, today will be as far from Wednesday as today was from Wednesday when the day before yesterday was tomorrow. What is the day after this day?

5. Five pieces of coal, a carrot and a scarf are lying on the lawn. Nobody put them on the lawn but there is a perfectly logical reason why they should be there. What is it?

SOLUTIONS

5. They were used by children who made a snowman. The snow has now melted!

4. Thursday.

3. Nine o'clock. Since there are twelve hours between the two times, half of that time equals six, then the halfway mark would have to be seven o'clock. If it were seven o'clock, two hours ago, the time would now be nine o'clock.

2. It's cheaper to take two friends at the same time. In this case, you would only be buying three tickets, whereas if you take the same friend twice you are buying four tickets.

1. No. This is a situation where you lose even if you win. Assuming your friend is being wise, they would take your £2 and say, "I lose", and give you £1 in return. You win the bet, but you're down £1!

WORDOODLES

Say what you see

Each of these Wordoodles is a word, phrase or saying, cunningly disguised! For example: minI'LL BE THEREute would mean: "I'll be there in a minute!" See how you get on with these...

1. k
   c
   u
   t
   s

2. bb
   mm
   uu
   hh
   tt

3. DAYdayOUT

4. ME
   AL

5. comp144etence

6. cover
   cop

7. mstickud

8. dumpdowndump

9. estimate me
   don't

10. dinner dinner
    table

SOLUTIONS

1. Stuck up. 2. Thumbs up. 3. Day in, day out. 4. Square meal. 5. Gross incompetence (144 in competence). 6. Undercover cop. 7. Stick in the mud. 8. Down in the dumps. 9. Don't underestimate me. 10. Dinner's on the table.

BACON & EGGS
Together Forever

Pair up these mixed groups with their natural partners.

CARS		
	Ford	Polo
	Audi	Cooper
	Vauxhall	Clio
	Volkswagen	TT
	Renault	Mondeo
	Mini	Vectra

COUNTRIES		
	Paris	Sweden
	Canberra	Germany
	Berlin	Italy
	Dublin	Australia
	Rome	France
	Stockholm	Ireland

CREATURES		
	Horse	Calf
	Rooster	Joey
	Kangaroo	Cub
	Cow	Cygnet
	Bear	Chick
	Swan	Foal

COLOURS		
	Green	Admiral
	Blue	Brick Road
	Yellow	Lagoon
	Red	Marmalade
	Orange	Medal
	Gold	Giant

SOLUTIONS

CARS: Ford Mondeo, Audi TT, Vauxhall Vectra, Volkswagen Polo, Renault Clio, Mini Cooper.
COUNTRIES: Paris France, Canberra Australia, Berlin Germany, Dublin Ireland, Rome Italy, Stockholm Sweden.
CREATURES: Horse Foal, Rooster Chick, Kangaroo Joey, Cow Calf, Bear Cub, Swan Cygnet.
COLOURS: Green Giant, Blue Lagoon, Yellow Brick Road, Red Admiral, Orange Marmalade, Gold Medal.

THINK DRINK!

Who's got what?

Al, Beth, and Cynthia got drinks at the cinema. "We want a small, a medium, and a large, and I don't get the large," Beth told the kid at the counter. "I thought you said you were getting large," said the boy who wanted the medium-size drink. Who wanted what size drink?

SOLUTION

Al got medium, Beth got small, and Cynthia got large. You know that Beth didn't want large, so she could have got small or medium. But you know that someone else wanted medium, so Beth had to get the small drink. You also know who got the medium-sized drink - it had to be Al, because he was the only boy in the group. Which means the large drink was for Cynthia.

LUCKY DIP
General Riddles

1. "I guarantee," said the salesman in the pet shop, "that this purple parrot will repeat every word it hears." A customer bought the bird, but found that the parrot wouldn't speak a single word. Nevertheless, what the salesman said was true. How could this be?

2. Jason was really excited when he saw his name on his friend's calendar. His friend pointed out that Jason's name is on every calendar. Can you figure out where?

3. Romeo and Juliet were dead in the middle of the room. All that surrounded them was a pool of water and some broken glass. What are Romeo and Juliet, and how did they die?

4. The expression, "Six of one, half a dozen of another," is commonly used to say that two alternatives are pretty much the same, because six and a half dozen are equal quantities. But are "six dozen dozen dozen" and "half a dozen dozen dozen" equal?

5. An old fashioned bike wheel has 21 spokes. How many spaces are between the spokes?

6. Six glasses are in a row. The first three are filled with milk, and the last three are empty. By moving only one glass, can you arrange them so that the full and the empty glasses alternate?

7. There is a square field. A guy walks around the field. It takes him 1 hour and 20 minutes to walk the first part, then 1 hour and 20 minutes to walk the second and third parts, but only 80 minutes to walk the fourth part. How does he do this without changing pace?

8. Gertrude Mills was horrified to find a fly in her tea. The waiter took her cup and went into the kitchen and returned with a fresh cup. She tasted it and shouted, "You brought me the same tea!" But how did she know?

9. A psychologist goes to a small village in Africa and decides to perform a scientific study comparing foot size to intelligence. He makes the discovery that in general, as foot size increases, so does intelligence. How can this be?

10. A murderer is condemned to death. He has to choose between three rooms. He is told the first is full of raging fires, the second is full of mad assassins with loaded guns, and the third is full of huge lions that haven't eaten in three years. Which room should he choose?

SOLUTIONS

10. The third. Lions that haven't eaten in three years are going to be dead.

9. He is measuring everyone's feet, including the feet of the very small children. So the statistics will show that larger feet belong to the smarter people... the adults.

8. She had already put sugar in it. When she tasted the new tea it was already sweet.

7. Because 80 minutes is the same as 1 hour and 20 minutes.

6. Pick up the second glass and pour the milk into the fifth glass and then put it back in the second position.

5. Twenty-one. (Most people will assume it will be one more or one less but you can draw it out to find the truth!)

4. No. Six dozen dozen is 6 x 12 x 12 x 12. A half dozen dozen is just 6 x 12 x 12.

3. Romeo and Juliet were goldfish, and their goldfish bowl was knocked over.

1. The parrot was deaf. 2. He was looking at the first letters of these months: July, August, September, October, November!

PIGGY IN THE MIDDLE

Word Links

Find the new word in each case that follows the first word and goes before of the second, making two new words or phrases. For example - Watch Collar - Adding DOG in the middle makes WATCHDOG and DOG COLLAR

COLOURS
Putting Keeper
Shocking Elephant
Penny Board
Navy Bottle
Charlie Owl
Lemon Submarine

VEGETABLES
Mashed Crisp
Red Patch
Split Shooter
Pop Cob
Baked Pole
Red Pot

INSECTS
Soldier Eater
Queen Hive
Volkswagen Juice
Fruit Paper
Wood Hole
Test Ball

MUSICAL INSTRUMENTS
Grand Stool
Ear Kit
Cow Ringer
Mouth Grinder
Car Pipe
Baby Snake

SOLUTIONS

COLOURS: Putting-Green-Keeper, Shocking-Pink-Elephant, Penny-Black-Board, Navy-Blue-Bottle, Charlie-Brown-Owl, Lemon-Yellow-Submarine.
VEGETABLES: Mashed-Potato-Crisp, Red-Cabbage-Patch, Split-Pea-Shooter, Pop-Corn-cob, Baked-Bean-Pole, Red-Pepper-Pot.
INSECTS: Soldier-Ant-Eater, Queen-Bee-Hive, Volkswagen-Beetle-Juice, Fruit-Fly-Paper, Wood-Worm-Hole, Test-Cricket-Ball.
MUSICAL INSTRUMENTS: Grand-Piano-Stool, Ear-Drum-kit, Cow-Bell-Ringer, Mouth-Organ-Grinder, Car-Horn-Pipe, Baby-Rattle-Snake.

NOT A PENNY MORE!

You're the Boss

You want to hire a temporary employee for one month. You offer him reasonable wages, but the employee suggests an alternative. For the first day of work, he will be paid a penny. For the second day, two pennies. For the third day, four pennies. The salary for each subsequent day will be double the previous day's, until the one month is over. Would it be a good idea to accept the potential employee's proposal?

SOLUTION

No way! He'll earn $5,368,709.12p on the thirtieth day alone!

FIGURE IT OUT
Mathematical Puzzles

1. What is the value of 1/2 of 2/3 of 3/4 of 4/5 of 5/6 of 6/7 of 7/8 of 8/9 of 9/10 of 1,000?

2. There was a shipwreck at sea and Buck, Lance and Jack were washed ashore on a small island. Reaching the shore, exhausted, they all fell asleep. Buck woke first and saw that a box of bananas had been washed ashore. He ate one third of the bananas and went back to sleep. Next, Lance woke up an seeing the box of bananas, ate one third of what was left and fell asleep. Jack woke up next and assumed that the other two hadn't eaten any bananas, so he ate one third of what remained. When Jack had finished, there were eight bananas left over. How many bananas were in the box originally?

3. A man was going on a one-way bus trip. He intended to ride for a certain distance, get off the bus and walk back to town. If the bus travels at a rate of nine miles per hour and he was to jog back to town at a rate of three miles per hour, how far would he ride so that he'd be back in eight hours?

SOLUTIONS

1. One hundred. By working backwards, the answer becomes easy. Nine-tenths of a thousand is nine hundred and eight-ninths of nine hundred is eight hundred etc., all the way down to the final answer of one hundred.
2. 27. If eight were left, it would represent two-thirds of the amount Jack found. Therefore, Lance left 12, and if 12 represented two-thirds of the amount Lance found, then he found 18. Since 18 represents two-thirds of the original amount, there must have been 27 originally.
3. Eighteen miles. Since he is riding three times as fast as he can jog, three quarters of his time must be spent jogging. Since he rode for two hours, travelling 18 miles, and jogged for six hours, travelling at three mph he made the round trip in eight hours.

WRITE STUFF

Word Puzzles & Teasers

1. Can you find the English word that can be formed from all these letters?

PNLLEEEESSSSS.

2. How would you rearrange the letters in the words "new door" to make one word?

3. Can you translate the following sentence to make a compliment?
Y Y U R Y Y U B I C U R Y Y 4 M E

4. What English word can have the last four of its five letters removed and still be pronounced the same way?

5. Using the words DROVES and NEWS write seven words using each letter once.

Rearrange the following to make seven top premiership football teams

6. Eel cash
7. An oval list
8. Humans to top
9. Dude e listen
10. Seal ran
11. Prove lilo
12. Wee mutant dish

SOLUTIONS

1. SLEEPLESSNESS. 2. Rearranging "new door" you get "one word" 3. Too wise you are, too wise you be, I see you are too wise for me! 4. Queue. 5. Seven words! 6. Chelsea. 7. Aston Villa. 8. Southampton. 9. Leeds United. 10. Arsenal. 12. West Ham United.

MATCH OF THE DAY
Matchstick Puzzles

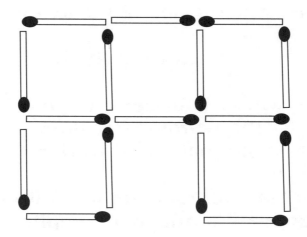

Move three matches to make four equal
touching squares.

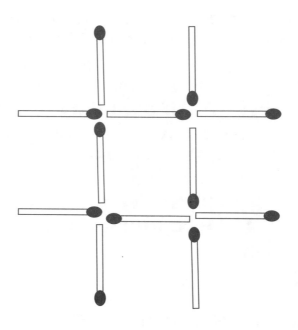

Move three matches to leave three equal
touching squares.

Answers on page 158

ABOUT TURN!

Privates on Parade

**A group of soldiers were standing in the blistering sun facing due west. Their sergeant shouted at them:
Right turn! About turn! Left turn!**

In which direction are they now facing?

SOLUTION

East! A right turn is 90 degrees, an about turn is 180 degrees, and a left turn is also 90 degrees. Therefore, the soldiers are now facing east.

MEGAMIX

Anagrams

Each of these mixed-up words (anagrams) can be unscrambled to make something that fits in each category. For example, if the category was ICE CREAM FLAVOURS and the anagram was TEACH COOL, the answer would be CHOCOLATE.

BOARD GAMES

Loom pony
A citron yip
Leo Cud
Virtual Stir it up

OCCUPATIONS

Burp elm
Ark be
Ted isn't
Chin came

TOOLS

Harm me
Wack ash
Nepal
Ric drew revs

COLOURS

Romano
Quite sour
Gear on
Lend rave

SINGERS (BOYS)

Mine me
I try rink mac
Is genial esquire
I blew a limbo, sir

SINGERS (GIRLS)

Persist, Barney
Moan, Dan
Jeep zen florin
Oddi

SOLUTIONS

PANTS ON FIRE!
Who's telling the truth?

1. Isaac and Albert were excitedly describing the result of the Third Annual International Science Fair Extravaganza in Sweden. There were three contestants, Louis, René, and Johannes.

Isaac reported that Louis won the fair, while René came in second. Albert, on the other hand, reported that Johannes won the fair, while Louis came in second. In fact, neither Isaac nor Albert had given a correct report of the results of the science fair. Each of them had given one correct statement and one false statement. What was the actual placing of the three contestants?

2. Captain Frank and some of the boys were exchanging old war stories. Art Bragg offered one about how his grandfather led a battalion against a German division during World War I. Through brilliant manoeuvres he defeated them and captured valuable territory.

After the battle he was presented with a sword bearing the inscription "To Captain Bragg for Bravery, Daring and Leadership. World War I. From the Men of Battalion 8."

Captain Frank looked at Art and said, "You really don't expect anyone to believe that yarn, do you?"

What's wrong with the story?

SOLUTIONS

1. Johannes won; René came in second; Louis came in third.
2. The inscription on the sword mentions World War I, but nobody called it World War I until there had been a World War II!

SHORT & SWEET
Figures of Speech

Each of these phrases has been shortened to just numbers and initials. For example: 26 = L of the A would be "26 Letters of the Alphabet". We'll supply a few clues. See how you get on with these...

1. 200 = P for P G in M
   Clue: Board game

2. 1 = W on a U
   Clue: Circus

3. 7 = W of the W
   Clue: Buildings

4. 101 = D in the D M
   Clue: Cruella

5. 1760 = Y in a M
   Clue: Distance

6. 15 P in a R U T
   Clue: Try

7. 14 D in a F
   Clue: Time

8. 12 D of C
   Clue: Partridge

9. 1 or 2 H on a C
   Clue: Desert

10. 5 L in a L
    Clue: Poem

SOLUTIONS

1. 200 Pounds for Passing Go in Monopoly. 2. 1 Wheel on a Unicycle. 3. 7 Wonders of the World. 4. 101 Dalmatians in the Disney Movie. 5. 1760 Yards in a Mile. 6. 15 Players in a Rugby Union Team. 7. 14 Days in a Fortnight. 8. 12 Days of Christmas. 9. 1 or 2 Humps on a Camel. 10. 5 Lines in a Limerick.

DROODLES

Picture Puzzles

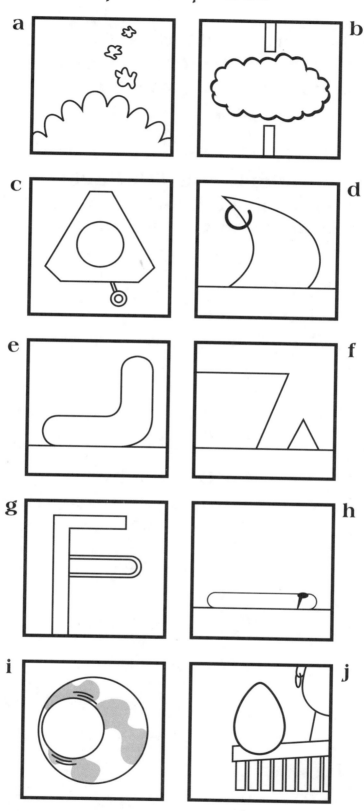

SOLUTIONS

a. Sheep smoking. b. Sheep crossing the road. c. Nelson smoking a pipe. d. Teenage Shark fin. e. Worm doing a sit up. f. Titanic & that iceberg. g. Trombone player behind a lamppost. h. Sunbathing worm. i. Worm's eye view of golf ball being potted. j. Young pirate's shoulder.

WORDOODLES

Say what you see

Some more Wordoodles. Once again,
each of these Wordoodles is a word,
phrase or saying which has been
cunningly disguised!
For example:

minI'LL BE THEREute
would mean: "I'll be there in a minute!"
See how you get on with these...

1. MEREPEAT

2. splostace

3. Gun Jr

4. hea / dac / he

5. go it it it it

6. cHIMp

7. ecnalg

8. anotherONETHING

9. Nostuckwhere

10. A maiden
Bowl

SOLUTIONS

1. Repeat after me. 2. Lost in space. 3. Son of a gun.
4. Splitting headache. 5. Go for it. 6. Making a monkey out of him.
7. A backwards glance. 8. One thing after another.
9. Stuck in the middle of nowhere. 10. Bowl a maiden over.

SPY PHONE

The Numbers of Nations

**Otto Von Hapsblunk - International Spy - has bugged the telephones of embassies all around the world.
Can you figure out which countries he can listen into by dialling the following numbers on his spy phone?**

**a. 381723 b. 4386170
c. 975932 891938
d. 898851 e. 87994 138521
f. 198981651 g. 80590386172
h. 77899416
i. 184379571 j. 730 0316172**

SOLUTIONS

a. France. b. Germany. c. United States.
d. Russia. e. South Africa. f. Australia. g. Switzerland.
h. Portugal. i. Argentina. j. New Zealand.

DUMB & DUMBER

How stupid do you feel?

This is a selection of tricky riddles that might make you feel stupid when you hear the answers!

1. If, having only one match, on a freezing winter day, you entered a room which contained a lamp, a paraffin heater, and a wood-burning stove, which should you light first?

2. Jeff had 17 rings and all but 9 were dropped down the drain, how many did he have left?

3. An electric train is travelling southwest at 95 miles per hour, and the wind is blowing north east at 95 miles per hour. In which direction does the steam blow?

4. Last summer, Mark bet his friends during a midnight feast in the garden, that the weather in exactly one week's time would not be sunny. How could Mark be so sure?

5. Which is correct - eight and eight IS fifteen or eight and eight ARE fifteen?

6. There are twelve 26p stamps in a dozen, but how many 52p stamps are there in a dozen?

7. Why do fish live in salt water?

8. A peacock laid an egg on top of the barn roof facing east. Which way will it roll?

9. Which is correct?

a. The Second Millennium began Jan. 1, 2000.

b. The Second Millennium began Jan. 1, 2001.

10. A horse is tied to a five-metre rope, and six metres away from it is a bale of hay. Without breaking the rope, the horse was able to get to the bale of hay. How is this possible?

11. A guy bet his neighbour a hundred pounds that his dog could jump higher than a house. Thinking this not possible, the neighbour took the bet and lost. Why did he lose the bet?

12. Which is it correct to say: the yolk of most eggs are white, or the yolk of most eggs is white?

13. There are two coins that total 11p, and one of them is not a 10p coin. How is this possible?

14. There's a bungalow with a purple kitchen, a purple bathroom and two purple bedrooms. So what colour were the stairs?

15. Which was the first planet to be discovered?

SOLUTIONS

1. You'd light the match first, of course! 2. Nine! 3. There isn't any steam. It is an electric train! 4. Because in exactly one week's time from the midnight feast it will be midnight again, so the sun will not be shining! 5. Neither. Eight and eight equals SIXTEEN! 6. Twelve! 7. Because pepper makes them sneeze! 8. It won't roll at all – peacocks don't lay eggs, the peahen lays them! 9. Neither is correct. The second millennium began January 1, 1001! 10. The other end of the rope isn't tied to anything! 11. Easy. Houses can't jump! 12. Neither. The yolk of most eggs is YELLOW! 13. The other one of them is a 10p coin! 14. There are no stairs in a bungalow! 15. Earth!

FIGURE IT OUT

Mathematical Puzzles

1. Which clock works best, the one that loses a minute a day, or the one that doesn't work at all?

2. If two hours ago it was as long after one o'clock in the afternoon as it was before one o'clock in the morning. What time would it be now?

3. Alice, Ben, Charlie, David, and Ed entered a contest to guess how many jelly beans are in a jar. Alice guessed 30, Ben guessed 28, Charlie guessed 29, David guessed 25, and Ed guessed 26. Two were off the mark by 1, one was wrong by 4, and one by 3. But one was correct. How many jelly beans are in the jar at the store?

4. Eight years ago, Sam was eight times the age of his son Sam Jr. Today, if you add their ages together, they add up to 52. How old are Sam and his son?

5. How many times do the hour and minute hand cross each other in a twelve hour period?

SOLUTIONS

5. Eleven times.

3. There are 29 jelly beans in the jar. 4. Sam is 40, and Sam Jr. is 12.

the time would now be nine o'clock.

o'clock, if it were seven o'clock, two hours ago,

half of that time is six, then the halfway mark would have to be seven

2. Nine o'clock. Since there are twelve hours between the two times, and

(losing 720 minutes or 12 hours).

but the one that loses a minute a day will not be correct again for 720 days

1. The one that doesn't work is best as it will always be correct twice a day,

THE OLD HEAVE HO

A Knotty Problem

Under what conditions would a rope be most likely to break?

a. 20 men of equal strength with 10 men pulling on each end.

b. 10 of the same men pulling on one end and the other end being fastened to a tree.

c. It makes no difference.

SOLUTION

The answer is c. If 20 men pull on the rope (10 on each end), the stress on the rope will be no greater than if 10 pulled from one end and the other was tied to a tree. The tension on a rope is no greater than the pull at one of its ends.

PANTS ON FIRE!
Who's telling the truth?

1. A traveller, on the way to the city, came to a fork in the road and didn't know which road to take. Standing at the fork were two men. Next to them was a sign stating that one of the two men always told the truth and one of the men always told lies (but it was not known which was which). The sign said that travellers could ask only one of the men one question, and the answer can be only "Yes" or "No". Which question could the traveller ask to find out the correct route?

a) Is the left road the wrong road to get to the city?
b) Is the left road the correct road for the city?
c) Would your friend say the left road was the correct one to the city?

2. Villains always lie and good guys always tell the truth. You see three men on the road and you ask the first one "What are you, a villain or a good guy?" You cannot make out his mumbled answer so you ask the second man. "What did he say?" The second man responds "He said he is a villain." The third man says "The second man is lying." What is each of the men — a good guy or a villain?

SOLUTIONS

1. c) Ask one of the men what the other man would answer to the question, "Is the left road the correct road for the city?" Then assume the answer you are given is false and act on that knowledge.
If the man you ask is the liar, he'll incorrectly give you the truthful man's answer. If the man you ask is the truthful man, he'll correctly give you the liar's wrong answer.

2. First man is a good guy. Second man is a good guy. Third man is a villain. If the first man was a good guy, then he would have told the truth and said that he was a good guy. If the first man was a villain then he would have lied and said that he was a good guy. The first man could not have said he was a villain and since the second man is lying, so the second man is a villain. The third man is telling the truth, thus he is a good guy. And since the second man was lying when he said that the first man said he was a villain, the first man must be a good guy!

136

PIGGY IN THE MIDDLE

Word Links

Find the new word in each case that
follows the first word and goes before of
the second, making two new words or
phrases. For example:
Watch Collar
Adding DOG in the middle makes
WATCHDOG and DOG COLLAR

ANIMALS
Siamese Burglar
Polar Hug
Mickey Trap
Jack Hutch
Sea Shoe
Cricket Man

NAMES
Ricky Sheen
Elton Travolta
Boy Clooney
Annie Lewis
George Douglas
James Diaz

WORLD
Planet Worm
Disney Rover
Magnetic Mouse
Arctic Liner
Family House
Sahara Boots

THE BODY
Bare Path
Back Stand
Hot Cold
Gold Bowl
Cauliflower Drum

SOLUTIONS

ANIMALS: Siamese-Cat-Burglar. Polar-Bear-Hug. Mickey-Mouse-Trap.
Jack-Rabbit-Hutch. Sea-Horse-Shoe. Cricket-Bat-Man.
NAMES: Ricky-Martin-Sheen. Elton-John-Travolta. Boy-George-Clooney.
Annie-Lennox-Lewis. George-Michael-Douglas. James-Cameron-Diaz.
WORLD: Planet-Earth-Worm. Disney-Land-Rover. Magnetic-Field-Mouse.
Arctic-Ocean-Liner. Family-Tree-House. Sahara-Desert-Boots.
THE BODY: Bare-Foot-Path. Back-Hand-Stand. Hot-Head-cold.
Gold-Finger-Bowl. Cauliflower-Ear-Drum.

APPLIANCE OF SCIENCE

Scientific Puzzles

1. Scientist Sue is travelling by ship from south of the equator to the north. She has a nice little cabin with a bathroom, but no window. Sue has no compass or other instruments — just the general luggage one brings on board a long cruise. Yet, without leaving her room or talking with anyone, Sue will be able to tell when the ship has crossed the equator. How?

2. Which would see most clearly in total darkness: a bat, a cat, or an owl?

3. What the first man-made object to break the sound barrier?

4. When Ashley was six years old she hammered a nail into her favourite tree to mark her height. Ten years later at age sixteen, Ashley returned to see how much higher the nail was. If the tree grew by five centimetres each year, how much higher would the nail be?

5. Which is heavier, a pound of feathers or a pound of gold?

SOLUTIONS

1. Sue can fill the sink and watch it drain. When the water reverses direction when going down the drain, she will know they have crossed the equator.
2. None. In total darkness it is impossible to see anything.
3. A whip. The noise of the crack of a whip is the result of the tip breaking the sound barrier.
4. The nail would be at the same height: trees grow from the top.
5. A pound of feathers. The more usual answer to this old chestnut is that both weigh a pound, but the fact is: gold is a precious metal and is therefore weighed in the Troy system of measurement rather than the Imperial one. This means that a pound of gold weighs only 12 ounces and a pound of feathers weighs 16 ounces.

138

SHOW US A SIGN!

Crossroads Collision

Jack and Joe were on vacation and driving along a deserted country road from the town of Kaysville to the town of Lynnsville. They came to a multiple fork in the road. The sign-post had been knocked down and they were faced with choosing one of five different directions. Since they had left their map at the last gas station and there was no one around to ask, how could Jack and Joe find their way to Lynnsville?

SOLUTION

They need to stand the signpost up so that the arm reading Kaysville points in the direction of Kaysville, the town they had just come from. With one arm pointing the correct way, the other arms will also point in the right directions.

CLEVER TREVOR

He's so smart it hurts!

1. A "Wise King" devised a contest to see who would receive the Princess's hand in marriage. The Princess was put in the middle a 50-foot square room with a big square carpet on the floor. Each of four suitors, including Clever Trevor, were put in one corner of the room with a small box to stand on. The first one to touch the Princess's hand would be declared the winner and become the new King.
The rules of the test were that the contestants could not walk over the carpet, cross the plane of the carpet, or hang from anything; nor could they use anything but their body and wits (i.e. no magic or telepathy, nor any items such as ladders, block and tackles, etc).
Trevor figured out a way. He married the Princess and became the new King. How did he figure it out?

2. One teenager goes up to a food booth at a fair and says, "A cola, please." Trevor, working the booth asks, "Regular or diet?"
The teenager asks, "What's the difference?" and is told that the regular costs 90 pence but that the diet costs a pound. The teenager says, "Give me a diet cola, please," and places a pound on the counter. Next, another teenager comes up to the booth and says, "A cola, please," placing a pound on the counter. Trevor gives him a diet cola.
How did Trevor know which cola - regular or diet - the second teenager wanted?

3. Trevor is working at Wimbledon and he has just received three crates of tennis balls. Unfortunately, All three crates are wrongly labelled. He must to put these balls on Centre Court immediately, so he only has time to look at one ball from one crate. So, the problem is, can he correctly label the crates by removing only one ball from the crate of his choice?
Here are the wrongly labelled crates:
White Tennis Balls
Yellow Tennis Balls
White & Yellow Tennis Balls

4. Trevor meets a man one day who asks him to try an experiment. The man puts three cards face down on a table. One is a jack and two are aces. He knows the order but Trevor doesn't. Trevor is allowed to ask the man one yes or no question, but when he asks it, he must point to one of the cards. If he points to an ace, the man will tell Trevor the truth, if he points to the jack, he may lie. Trevor has to find one of the aces... What question does he ask?

SOLUTIONS

1. Trevor simply asked the Princess to walk over to him and touch his hand.

2. The second teenager put a pound in change on the counter: a fifty-pence piece, two twenty-pence pieces and a ten-pence piece.
If the teenager had wanted a regular cola, he wouldn't have put the ten pence piece on the counter.

3. The one thing to keep in mind is that EVERY box is mislabelled.
Trevor starts by taking a tennis ball from the box labelled "White & Yellow Tennis Balls." Let's say it's yellow. That must mean the box he got it from contains all yellow balls. He takes the "Yellow Tennis Balls" label and puts it on the box he just got the ball from. He takes the old "White & Yellow Tennis Balls" label and puts it on one of the remaining two boxes. But which one? If he puts it on the box that the "Yellow Tennis Balls" label came from then that would mean that the box marked "White Tennis Balls" couldn't be changed and he knows EVERY box is known to be mislabelled.
So, he moves the "White Tennis Balls" label to the unlabelled box and puts the "White & Yellow Tennis Balls" label on the box that was labelled "White Tennis Balls." If the ball removed from the first box had been white then the same logic would prevail in moving the labels around.

4. He points to the middle card and says, "Is the card to the right an ace?" If the answer is yes then the card on the right is an ace. If the answer is no, then it's a jack and the card on the left is an ace. This solution works because if he's pointing to an ace the man will tell the truth, and if he's pointing to the jack the answer doesn't matter anyway because both left and right are going to be the aces.

WRITE STUFF
Word Puzzles & Teasers

1. Can you work out the reasoning behind the order of girls' and boys' names in the lists below?
Girls: Heather, Ellen, Laura, Anne, Nancy.
Boys: Andy, Ted, Mike, Dick, Vic.

2. A palindrome is a word (or phrase or sentence) that reads the same from left to right as it does from right to left. For example, a palindrome that means "trick or joke" is "gag". For each of the clues below, see if you can find an answer that's a palindrome.

2a. Midday
2b. Polite thing to call a lady
2c. Flat, not tilting one way or the other
2d. Take a sneaky look
2e. You have two on your face
2f. Something that fails to work
2g. A concert played by a band
2h. Move down-and-up in water
2i. Baby dog
2j. What a baby wears at dinner

3. Assign every letter of the alphabet its numerical value: A=1, B=2 and so on. Which of these vegetable names has the lowest score when the numerical values are added up: Pea, Cabbage, Leek, Bean?

SOLUTIONS

3. Cabbage - 21, Pea - 22, Bean - 22, Leek - 33.
2f. dud. 2g. gig. 2h. bob. 2i. pup. 2j. bib.
2a. noon. 2b. madam. 2c. level. 2d. peep. 2e. eye.
is the last letter of the following name.
of the next. In the list of boys' names, the second-to-last letter in each name
1. In the list of girls' names, the second letter of each name is the first letter

HORSING AROUND
The Helpful Neighbour

A man on his deathbed tells his three sons he will leave them his horses. To the eldest son he leaves half of his horses. To his second son he leaves one third of them, and to his youngest, he leaves one ninth. After he passed away, the three sons went to get their horses, but discovered there were 17 animals. They did not want to sell or kill any of the horses, and they could not think of a way to divide the horses exactly as their father wished. Just then their neighbour came riding along on his horse and listened to their problem. Immediately the neighbour thought of a clever solution to the division problem that suited everyone.

SOLUTION

The neighbour added his horse to the sons' horses, which brought the total to 18. Then the oldest son took half, which is 9, the second son took 6, which is one third, and the youngest took 2, which is one ninth — the total being 17. The neighbour then rode off on the same horse he arrived with.

LET'S GET PHYSICAL
Practical Problems

1. Put a coin in a bottle and then stop the opening with a cork. How can you get the coin out of the bottle without pulling out the cork or breaking the bottle?

2. One day, Charlie was driving his car when he got a flat tyre. While changing the tyre, he accidently dropped all four nuts from the wheel through a drain in the road. After banging his head several times on the roof of his car for being so careless, he attached his spare tyre the only way he knew how and drove to the nearest service station to repair his flat and replace the lost nuts. How did he attach the spare tyre?

3. How can you hold onto both ends of a rope and tie a knot in the rope without letting go of either end of the rope?

4. How can you clasp someone's hands together in such a manner that they cannot walk away without unclasping them?

5. James ordered a fishing rod, priced at £3.56. Unfortunately, James lives in a very remote part of Greenland and the import rules there forbid any package longer than 4 feet to be imported.
The fishing rod was 4 feet and 1 inch, just a little too long, so how can the fishing rod be mailed to James without breaking the rules?
Ideally James would like the fishing rod to arrive in one piece!

6. Picture an empty wine bottle with a cork secured at the top in the usual way. Inside the bottle a metal ring hangs suspended by a string.
How is it possible to make the metal ring drop to the bottom of the bottle without touching the ring, the thread, the cork, or the bottle while leaving the cork in place and intact?

7. Sally and her younger brother, Billy, were fighting as usual. Their mother was tired of the pair of them, and decided to punish them. Her fiendish punishment was to make them stand on the same piece of newspaper in such a way that they couldn't touch each other.
How did she accomplish this?

8. In a farmer's field, there are two vertical 750-foot tall posts. The posts have a 1,000-foot rope stretched between their topmost points.
The rope sags to within 250 feet of the ground.
How far apart are the posts?

SOLUTIONS

1. Push the cork into the bottle, and shake the coin out.
2. He removed one nut from each of his good wheels leaving three nuts on each tyre, including the spare.
3. Cross your arms before grabbing onto each end of the rope. When you uncross your arms, there will be a knot in the rope.
4. Put their hands around a lamp-post.
5. Insert the fishing rod into a box which measures 4 feet on all sides, the fishing rod will fit within the diagonal of the box with room to spare.
6. By using a magnifying glass and the sun's rays you could burn through the string and consequently cause the ring to drop to the bottom of the bottle.
7. Sally's mother slid a newspaper under a door and made Sally stand on one side of the door and her brother on the other.
8. Zero ft. The rope sags 500ft from the top of the post to make it 250ft, above the ground. Since the rope is 1,000ft it must be folded directly in half which would happen only if the two posts were right next to each other.

145

LUCKY DIP
General Riddles

1. Mary was making apricot jam. She put all the apricots in the pot and stirred them up. Then she remembered she had to add one ounce of lemon juice for every two apricots. How did she figure out exactly how much lemon juice to put in the pot?

2. A 6-foot tall magician had a water glass and was holding the glass above his head. He let it drop to the carpet without spilling a single drop of water. How could he manage to drop the glass from a height of six feet and not spill a drop of water?

3. Two fathers and two sons went fishing one day. They were there the whole day and caught only three fish. One father said, "That is enough for all of us, we will have one each."
How can this be possible?

4. Since a person uses about the same amount of energy walking 2 miles as they would running for 2 miles, would a person use more energy running for 10 minutes, walking for 10 minutes, or the same amount of energy?

5. If boiling water is poured into a thick drinking glass as well as into a very thin wine glass, of the two, which is more likely to crack?

SOLUTIONS

1. She counted the apricot stones. 2. The glass was empty.

3. There was the father, his son, and his son's son.

4. Since a person running for 10 minutes would cover more distance than walking for 10 minutes, he/she would use more energy running for 10 minutes.

5. The thick glass is more likely to crack since glass is a poor conductor of heat. In a thin glass, the heat passes more quickly from the glass into the surrounding air, causing the glass to expand equally. When hot water is poured into a thick glass, the inner surface expands, but the outer surface does not. It is this extreme stress on the glass that causes it to crack.

HOT DIGGETIN DOG!
Find Ralph's Bone

Ralph the dog can't remember where he buried his bone - under the rock, in the garden, under the porch, or under the tree. If only one of the following sentences is true, where is Ralph's bone?

1. The bone is under the rock.
2. The bone is in the garden or under the tree.
3. The bone is under the rock or under the porch.
4. The bone is not in the garden.

SOLUTION

The bone is in the garden.

If sentence 1 is true, then only one sentence can be true, so both 1 and 3 are true. That leaves the garden and the tree, so let's look at sentences 2 and 4. If sentence 2 is true, then sentence 4 is false. That would leave us with just 1 sentence, but is the bone in the garden or under the tree? We know that sentence 4 is false, so the bone must be in the garden.

LUCKY DIP
General Riddles

1. Answer the following question with a simple "yes" or "no".
If the day before the day after the day before today was hotter than the day after the day before today, was the day before today hotter than today?

2. Sarah went to get her driving licence. When asked her age, she replied: "My age today is three times what it will be three years from now minus three times what my age was three years ago."
How old is Sarah?

3. If you were blindfolded and placed in front of a large bowl containing lots of £50, £20, £10 and £5 notes, and you were allowed to take one note at a time until you have taken four notes of the same value, what would be the largest total amount of money you could draw?

4. A man walks into a his bathroom and shoots himself right between the eyes using a real gun with real bullets. He walks out alive, with no blood anywhere. He didn't miss and he wasn't Superman or any other caped crusader.
How did he do this?

SOLUTIONS

1. Yes. The day before the day after the day before today was yesterday. The day after the day before today is today. And the day before today was yesterday. So yes, yesterday was hotter than today.

2. Sarah is 18. If she is 18 then three years from now would be 21x3 (63). Three times her age three years ago would be 15x3 (45). Subtract 45 from 63 and she is 18.

3. £305. You could take 3 - £50's, 3 - £20's, 3 - £10's, 3 - £5's, and the last draw would be another £50 note.

4. He shot his reflection in the bathroom mirror.

148

MEGAMIX
Anagrams

Each of these mixed-up words (anagrams) can be unscrambled to make something that fits in each category. For example, if the category was ICE CREAM FLAVOURS and the anagram was TEACH COOL, the answer would be CHOCOLATE

DINOSAURS

Near a runty ox russ
I do old cups
Sour at guess
On USA or burst

ZODIAC SIGNS

Sis at guitar
I carp corn
I'm Geni
Coop, Sir?

BRITISH TOWNS

Drub Hinge
Sean Saw
Self Bat
Ah bin Grimm

FOOTBALL TEAMS

Ham flu
Oliver lop
Eddie lent us
Entertained chums

FRUIT

Alpine Pep
A green tin
Lent me a row
Fear rug pit

COUNTRIES

A trial USA
Nan, we'd laze
Ran wild zest
Polar tug

SOLUTIONS

COUNTRIES: Australia, New Zealand, Switzerland, Portugal
FRUIT: Pineapple, Tangerine, Watermelon, Grapefruit.
FOOTBALL TEAMS: Fulham, Liverpool, Leeds United, Manchester United.
BRITISH TOWNS: Edinburgh, Swansea, Belfast, Birmingham.
ZODIAC SIGNS: Sagittarius, Capricorn, Gemini, Scorpio.
DINOSAURS: Tyrannosaurus Rex, Diplodocus, Stegosaurus, Brontosaurus.

149

WHAT THE DICKENS?

Puzzles that confuse

1. Do this in your head, not on paper!
Take 1,000 and add 40 to it.
Now add another 1,000.
Now add 30. And another 1,000.
Now add 20. Now add another 1,000.
Now add 10. What is the total?

2. Read the sentence below and count the
F's in that sentence.
Count them only once.
Don't go back and count them again.
FINISHED FILES ARE THE RESULT OF
YEARS OF SCIENTIFIC STUDY
COMBINED WITH
THE EXPERIENCE OF YEARS.

3. A bookworm eats from the first page of
a set of encyclopaedias to the last page.
The bookworm eats in a straight line.
The set of encyclopaedias consists of ten
1,000-page books and is sitting on a
bookshelf in the correct number order.
Not counting covers, title pages, etc.,
how many pages does the bookworm
eat through?

SOLUTIONS

1. Did you get 5000? OK, so do most people.
But the correct answer is 4100! Check it with your calculator....

2. A person of average intelligence finds three of them.
If you spotted four, you're above average. If you got five, you did well. If you
caught six, you are a genius.
There is no catch.
Many people forget the "of"s.
The human brain tends to see them as V's and not F's.
There are actually SIX F's in the sentence.

3. On a bookshelf the first page of the first volume is on the "inside"
so the bookworm eats only through the front cover of the first volume, then
8 times 1,000 pages of Volumes 2 - 9, then through the back cover to the
last page of Vol 10. He eats 8,000 pages.
If the bookworm ate the first page of Volume 1 and the last page of
Volume 10, it ate 8,000 pages.

A COUPLE OF SHOTS

A man walks into a bar

A man walks into a bar
and asks the bar-tender
for a glass of water.
The bar-tender reaches under the bar
and brings out a gun
and aims it at the man.
The man says,
"Thank you,"
and leaves.
What happened?

SOLUTION

The man had the hiccups and wanted a glass of water
to help get rid of them. The bar-tender could hear the hiccups
when the man spoke, so he brought the gun out
to scare the hiccups away.
It worked and the man thanked him and left,
no longer needing the glass of water.

WHAT AM I?

Mystery Objects

1. It is in the rock, but not in the stone;
It is in the marrow, but not in the bone;
It is in the bolster, but not in the bed;
It is not in the living, nor yet in the dead.
What is it?

2. You answer me, although I never ask
you questions. What am I?

3. I'm white & used for cutting & grinding.
When I'm damaged, humans usually
remove me or fill me. For most animals I
am a useful tool.
What am I?

4. I come in different shapes and sizes.
Part of me are curves, others are straight.
You can put me anywhere you like, but,
there is only one right place for me.
What am I?

5. When I point South it's bright, but when
I point North it's dark.
What am I?

6. I am the only thing that always tells the
truth. I show off everything that I see. I
come in all shapes and sizes.
So tell me what I must be!

7. Two bodies have I, though both joined
in one, the stiller I stand the faster I run.
What am I?

8. I can be cracked, I can be made.
I can be told, I can be played.
What am I?

9. My first is in ocean but never in sea,
my second's in wasp but never in bee.
My third is in glider and also in flight,
my whole is a creature that comes
out at night.
What am I?

10. The sun bakes me, the hand breaks
me, the foot treads on me, and the mouth
tastes me. What am I?

11. Take one out and scratch my head,
I am now black but once was red.
What am I?

12. What can be driven,
but has no wheels.
And can be sliced,
and still remain whole?

13. I start with the letter e,
I end with the letter e.
I contain only one letter,
Yet I am not the letter e!
What am I?

14. I turn around once.
What is out will not get in.
I turn around again.
What is in will not get out.
What am I?

15. Break it and it is better, immediately
set and harder to break again.
What is it?

SOLUTIONS

FIGURE IT OUT

Mathematical Puzzles

a. At a recent visit to the reptile house at the local zoo, I counted a total of 27 heads and 70 feet. I was counting snakes, lizards, and people. I know that there were exactly twice as many lizards as people. How many snakes did I count?

b. Brad Doe works for a packaging company. One day, he received four separate orders and accidently mixed up the addresses, so he applied the address labels at random. What is the probability that exactly three packages were correctly labelled?

c. There are two ducks in front of two other ducks. There are two ducks behind two other ducks. There are two ducks beside two other ducks. How many ducks are there?

d. If three cats catch three mice in three minutes, how many cats would be needed to catch 100 mice in 100 minutes?

e. If it takes Alicia 3 hours to paint a fence, and it takes Mark 6 hours to complete the same job, how long would it take both of them working together at their normal paces to complete the same job?

SOLUTIONS

a. 6 snakes, 7 people, and 14 lizards.

b. Zero. If three packages are correctly labeled, then so is the fourth.

c. Four (as shown below)
```
X X
X X
```

d. The same three would do. Since these three cats are averaging one mouse per minute, given 100 minutes, the cats could catch 100 mice.

e. Two hours. Alicia can complete 1/3 of the job in one hour and Mark can complete 1/6 of the job in one hour; therefore, together they can complete 1/3 plus 1/6 or 1/2 of the job in one hour. Consequently, the entire job can be completed in just two hours

BACON & EGGS
Together Forever

Pair up these mixed groups with their natural partners.

SPORTS

Martina Hingis	Athletics
Michael Jordan	Motor racing
Lennox Lewis	Tennis
Marion Jones	Soccer
Michael Schumacher	Boxing
Ronaldo	Basketball

STATES

Dallas	Florida
Los Angeles	Illinois
Miami	Hawaii
Chicago	Alaska
Anchorage	California
Honolulu	Texas

SITES

Pyramids	Greece
Eiffel Tower	Australia
Grand Canyon	France
Great Barrier Reef	Egypt
Acropolis	Italy
Colosseum	USA

STARS

Eddie Murphy	Titanic
Daniel Radcliffe	Chicken Run
Elijah Wood	Attack of the Clones
Leonardo DiCaprio	Shrek
Ewan Macgregor	Lord of the Rings
Mel Gibson	Harry Potter

SOLUTIONS

SPORTS: Martina Hingis Tennis, Michael Jordan Basketball, Lennox Lewis Boxing, Marion Jones Athletics, Michael Schumacher Motor racing, Ronaldo Soccer. STATES: Dallas Texas, Los Angeles California, Miami Florida, Chicago Illinois, Anchorage Alaska, Honolulu Hawaii. SITES: Pyramids Egypt, Eiffel Tower France, Grand Canyon USA, Great Barrier Reef Australia, Acropolis Greece, Colosseum Italy. STARS: Eddie Murphy Shrek, Daniel Radcliffe Harry Potter, Elijah Wood Lord of the Rings, Leonardo DiCaprio Titanic, Ewan Macgregor Attack of the Clones, Mel Gibson Chicken Run.

THINK ABOUT IT!

Puzzles that aren't what they seem

At first glance these puzzles seem difficult, but they're not.
In each case there is a simple solution.

1. A girl who was just learning to drive went down a one-way street in the wrong direction, but didn't break the law. How come?

2. Once a dog named Nelly lived on a farm. There were three other dogs on the farm. Their names were Blackie, Whitey, and Brownie. What do you think the fourth dog's name was?

3. The rope ladder of a boat hangs over the side of the boat and just reaches the water. Its rungs are 8 inches apart. How many rungs will be under the water when the tide rises 4 feet?

4. You are driving a bus. Four people get on, three people get off, then eight people get on and ten people get off, then six people get on and two more people get off. What colour were the bus driver's eyes?

5. Why are 2002 50p coins worth more than 2001 50p coins?

SOLUTIONS

1. She was walking. 2. Nelly.
(If there are only four dogs on the farm, the fourth one must be Nelly!)
3. When the tide rises 4 feet, the boat and its ladder will also rise.
So no rungs will be under the water.
4. Whatever colour your eyes are, because "You are driving the bus!"
5. Because 2002 50p coins are worth £1001 and 2001 50p coins are only worth £1000.50p.

ANSWERS

Answers to puzzles on page 24.

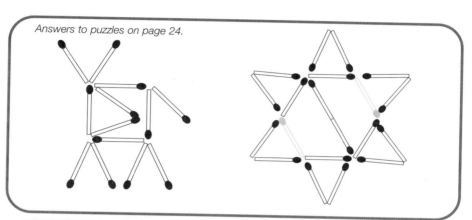

Answers to puzzles on page 51.

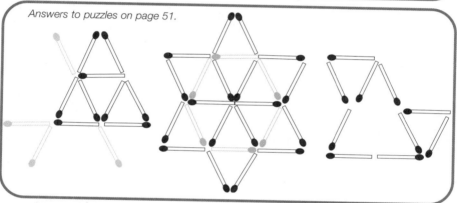

Answers to puzzles on page 76.

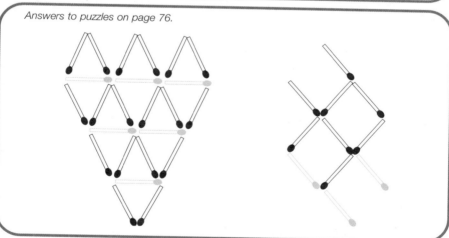

Answers to puzzles on page 103.

a   b   c

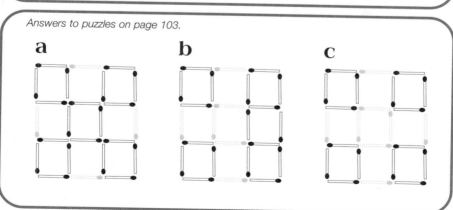

ANSWERS

Answers to puzzle on page 103.

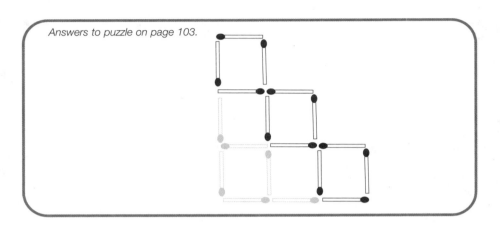

Answers to puzzles on page 124.

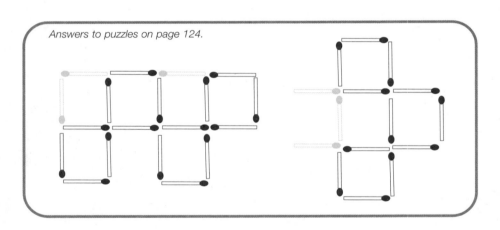

Answers to puzzles on page 80.

a.

b.

c.

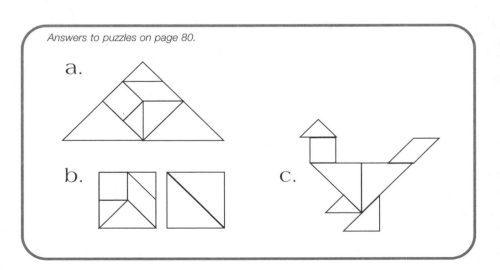

If you enjoyed this book, you can find more hilarious jokes, amazing facts, and brainbusting riddles and puzzles in the following books, also published by Dean:

Title	ISBN
The World's Funniest Animal Jokes for Kids	0 603 56064 4
The World's Funniest Disgusting Jokes for Kids	0 603 56065 2
The World's Funniest School Jokes for Kids	0 603 56063 6
The World's Most Amazing Animal Facts for Kids	0 603 56060 1
The World's Most Amazing Planet Earth Facts for Kids	0 603 56062 8
The World's Most Amazing Science Facts for Kids	0 603 56061X
1000 of the World's Funniest Jokes for Kids	0 603 56066 0
1000 of the World's Most Astonishing Facts for Kids	0 603 56067 9